PSYCHO-ENERGETICS™

A Method of Self-Discovery and Healing

Jordan P. Weiss, M.D.

Oceanview Publishing
P.O. Box 8708, Dept. 613
Newport Beach, CA 92658-1708

PSYCHOENERGETICS ™

A Method of Self-Discovery and Healing

By Jordan P. Weiss, M.D.

Published by:
Oceanview Publishing
P.O. Box 8708, Dept. 613
Newport Beach, CA 92658-1708

Printed in the United States of America
Second Edition 1995
First Edition 1994
ISBN: 0-9638640-2-5
Library of Congress Catalog Card Number: 95-090051

Cover Design by Robert Howard, Fort Collins, Colorado
Editing by PeopleSpeak, Laguna Hills, California
Illustrations by Craig Poulsen, Fountain Valley, California

To my parents, Millie and Vic

who have taught me to think for myself
and believe in myself.

ACKNOWLEDGMENTS

There are many who have motivated, encouraged, and taught me much along the way.

Special thanks to Bob Hilton, a master therapist and healer.

And thank you to Cheryl, Monie, Annie, Julie, and my "main" man, Ollie.

ABOUT THE AUTHOR

DR. JORDAN WEISS, Director of the Center for Psychoenergetic Therapy, is board certified in Psychiatry and Internal Medicine. He specializes in behavioral medicine, stress management, personal transformation and chronic illness. A pioneer in the field of holistic medicine, Dr. Weiss has been a featured talk show guest on television and radio.

His approach is based on the theory that our real and guiding emotions are unconscious and exist as energy patterns within us which we can learn to experience. Psychoenergetics is a systematic method which teaches an individual to interact with and master these emotional energy patterns for unlimited personal growth and healing.

Dr. Weiss holds memberships with the American Medical Association, the California Medical Association, the American Psychiatric Association, the Orange County Psychiatric Association, and the World Psychiatric Association.

He presents papers, gives workshops and lectures on psychoenergetics throughout the United States and Europe and maintains a private practice.

PREFACE

—to the Second Edition—

This book is about self-discovery. It is about discovering your deepest feelings and thoughts, and how knowing them will get you in control of your own life once again. The discovery of your real self will also lead to a healing of your mind and body through a process I call psychoenergetics.

Since the original printing I have received a great deal of feedback about how well many of these psychoenergetic techniques and concepts have worked and how gratified many were to work out a problem they had had for many years. In public lectures, which I often use to work and refine new ideas, I was amazed at how easily individuals were able to understand concepts and techniques in hours that I thought would have required much more training or study. I have also had a chance to give lectures about psychoenergetics in about a half-dozen European countries. The techniques were understood by non-native English speakers as well as those hearing it in translation. Now I know there are no limitations. It is exciting to have a chance to improve upon one's work and to make it more accessible and user-friendly.

For many years I used traditional psychotherapies, including hypnosis, quite extensively before I developed psychoenergetics. I found that they had three major limitations. First, they relied too much on the therapist and did not give enough knowledge to the individual to use on his or her own. Second, traditional psychotherapies lack a system. In other words, there is no logical sequential method to approach life problems, nor is there an accurate way to receive reliable feedback on one's progress. Third, and most important, psychotherapies do not acknowledge the truth of the relationships between the mind, body, and energy. Human beings are a complex combination of mental and physical energies. These energies follow precise laws and can be directed by our minds according to our intentions to achieve self-healing.

Self-help or self-healing sometimes has a connotation of less than real help. This seems especially true in the healing profession itself where amateurs are advised to "back off" lest they hurt themselves mentally and physically.

The scarcity of resources for health care, however, which will most certainly never improve, makes it ever more important that we care for ourselves both preventively as well as after the occurrence of a problem. Psychoenergetics is then one more way to achieve both goals, time efficiently and cost effectively, without a lot of additional effort.

For some, one more thing to do, after diet and exercise and all the chores of daily living, may seem to be just too much. I perfectly understand this; but I also know that the key to all health is loving yourself. And you love yourself best when you know your deepest feelings and desires and can express them. If you can give yourself 15 to 20 minutes a day to experience your own vital energies and express them, how can you not be stronger, happier, and healthier? Follow with me on this learning and healing journey and I promise you rich rewards for your efforts.

Jordan P. Weiss, M.D.
Newport Beach, California 1995

TABLE OF CONTENTS

INTRODUCTION

You often hear the expression, "Life is what you make it." This is basically true because we *do* make our lives (most of the time anyway). But sometimes it seems that our lives just happen and that we're not making them at all but are stuck in them. At those times, we have to ask ourselves, "Am I really stuck in my life, or do I just have the wrong attitude?"

Could changing your attitude really change your life? You may know a person who is hopeful in the face of adversity and disappointment. In some regard, someone who is positive even when confronted with sadness or disappointment could be said to have a good attitude. Your attitude is actually a reflection of something even more fundamental—your belief system. Beliefs are the rules and regulations under which you run your life. Beliefs, as you will come to see in this book, are really what determine the direction your life takes.

BECOMING AWARE OF ATTITUDES

As a boy, I became aware of attitude (belief) and its effect when an unusual event occurred in my neighborhood. An elderly rabbi was walking along the street with his wife when suddenly she collapsed. It was the Sabbath, and according to the Orthodox tradition, one is not allowed to ride in a mechanical vehicle during that period of time. Now here was a life-and-death emergency—something to truly challenge the rabbi's attitude (belief) toward Orthodox Judaism. He decided (though it was a terrible struggle) to carry his wife rather than call an ambulance or cab. His belief was that a law made by God is to be obeyed under any circumstance without exception.

The rabbi's decision was a result of very conscious religious beliefs, rules by which he chose to live—a system. All of us have systems too, whether or not they're aligned with a faith. Your "ism" is probably personal, which might be called "Steveism," "Maryism," or "Larryism." It is as much a religion as the rabbi's in the sense that you often follow very rigid rules that lead to certain outcomes. There is, however, one difference between you and the rabbi on this matter—his rules and beliefs are *known* to him. In all likelihood you are acting on rules and rituals in your personal "religion" that are unconscious or unknown to you. (If you're doubtful of this, I'll show you proof later in the book by asking you to look closely at yourself and your attitudes.) When you make important decisions without knowing your rules, then you're at a distinct disadvantage. If things aren't going well, you may not know why. You may even have tried to make something right that was going wrong but never seemed to succeed. Not knowing the rules of the game, as it were, can be a serious handicap. So if you find yourself wishing that the daily experience of your life—your marriage, job, health, and friendships—were different, you're having a problem.

DEVELOPING A WORKABLE SYSTEM

Solving the problem depends on having a workable system so that you can accurately assess the situation, examine your motives and goals, and take the necessary action. To move in the right direction requires that you know your true feelings and motivations. To do that you need to look inward, in a number of different ways, and draw information, such as your motivations, to help you solve the problem.

This book provides one system to help you find out more about yourself. Then, armed with your system, you can do what you feel is right. But you have an advantage over the rabbi—his system is essentially limited, like most "isms," whereas yours is unlimited—open. In an open system, any thought is encouraged and permissible. If any thought can be entertained or any feeling felt, then a solution becomes more readily possible. In this book I will encourage you to begin to think without limitation and question how your present beliefs and attitudes fit into your whole system. I want you to ask yourself, "Why do I believe this or that? How do I really know what the truth is and what to believe?" These and other issues will be taken up in the pages that follow.

In addition to asking the right questions to get the right answers, the system described here teaches that the mind has a number of abilities that are worth knowing. These include the ability to imagine and create inner visions to activate and affect the human body, to bring up relevant past experiences, and to give "computer-like" assessments when prompted by certain "commands" and "programs." This last innovation may be new to you, and I'm certain you'll find it most intriguing.

Regardless of how you use the system I describe here, you'll be able to see possibilities that didn't exist before. This system can be added to your existing system to enlarge it, and any portion of the book may be useful, depending on how much you wish to change. Some of the techniques can be used separately, but to give clarity and continuity to the entire system, I recommend that you begin reading from Chapter 1.

I have tried as much as possible to avoid vague terminology. In my opinion, this only serves to give the illusion of communication when none is taking place. Ultimately, I hope this system will help you to better know the "self within" and enjoy a healthier and happier life.

Good luck and God bless.

Jordan P. Weiss, M.D.
Newport Beach, California

CHAPTER I

THE HEALING POWER OF EMOTIONAL RELEASE

The lives we are living right now were created by specific, powerful, and profound feelings that exist deep down inside at an unconscious level, whether or not we choose to acknowledge them. Therefore, despite what we might think, we make choice X over Y in career or personal relationships because we *feel* it is the best choice rather than the most logical or rational one. Sometimes it's not possible to be logical or rational about the really important things, and we get stuck in a rut instead of creating lives that we desire.

The majority of my patients are very bright, insightful people who generally understand what is wrong with their thinking and often what life steps they need to take. If change were simply a matter of understanding, we could discuss it rationally and be done. The problem is that thinking straight and being insightful are not enough to change their feelings or behavior. Despite their best efforts, they can't shake their underlying feelings—of anger, abandonment, guilt, or other troubling emotions.

To effect real change, people need to be able to remove or release unwanted feeling states permanently. You will learn in this book that when you develop a true awareness of your deepest thoughts and feelings, and acknowledge and experience them within your body—even briefly—then unwanted feelings will be released rapidly. A change in thinking and an improved state of physical, emotional, and spiritual well-being will follow.

In this book, I will describe a way to master your own healing power using methods to facilitate permanent release of unwanted feelings. I will also show you how to understand your problems, issues, hang-ups, and challenges in an entirely new way.

By using this new method, which I call *psychoenergetics*, you will be able to understand why you think and feel as you do and how to change yourself in a very methodical and practical way. This book doesn't present a theory of personality or a solution to one type of problem, but deals with the true nature of feelings and thoughts. For this reason, what you learn here can be added to any existing therapy or self-help techniques, such as 12-step programs or inner child work.

EMOTIONAL ENERGY AND ITS EFFECTS

Have you ever been at a football or baseball game when the score was close, the crowd was cheering for victory, and the players seemed to put forth that extra effort to win the game? Did you feel like you were helping? Do you believe there is such a thing as a "home field advantage"? If you answered "yes" to either question, you'd be in the majority. Most people feel that fans have some effect on the players and, in turn, the outcome of the game. According to statistics, playing for the home crowd usually gives the team an advantage.

Some athletes are big favorites because they are known to have "heart," meaning they go beyond physical skill or training to achieve success, something we all find inspiring. The popularity of the *Rocky* movies indicates to me that people believe that strong desire, determination, and feelings make a difference.

Feelings are responsible for amazing things, such as people risking their own lives to save total strangers from burning buildings or rushing rivers. We all know the power of feeling and how it can motivate us to do great deeds.

There is another side to feeling—an ugly side. The energy of angry feelings can be fed and grow out of control when reflected and gathered up by an angry crowd. For example, fans are routinely killed at soccer games in Europe and South America when angry emotions are multiplied.

The April 1992 riots in Los Angeles illustrate another expression of infectious, angry emotional energy that can get out of control. It had to be forcefully contained to prevent further harm. Again, the riots demonstrated the power of emotion and the impact of negative energy that can be powerfully destructive.

Daily, we are bombarded by senseless crimes of violence committed towards strangers for no apparent motive. None of the people involved in violence want anything more than a happy, healthy, and fulfilling life just like you. The problem is that their emotions have completely overtaken them, and they have no way to diminish their intense anger and sadness to any significant degree so that their behavior can be more socially appropriate.

That same basic difficulty in properly identifying, diminishing, or releasing unwanted and unhelpful emotions is what keeps most human beings from the lives they desire. In order to achieve success in any area of life, we must first know how we really feel about it deep inside. We must know the proper way to handle any self-defeating feelings that might get in the way of our success.

One way to solve these problems is to view emotions as a powerful source of energy, like the sun or electricity or nuclear power. All of these energies have the ability to do both tremendous good and serious harm. We can then think about our feelings toward ourselves and others as dynamic movements of emotional energies.

For example, imagine that you were terrified to get on an elevator. We might try to solve the problem using several approaches. We could try to hypnotize away the phobia and make you believe that you aren't afraid. Or we could try to rationally discuss it or work back to some important, original event that marked the beginning of your fear. Another approach is to define the problem as *fear energy* generated in response to an image of an elevator. Certain techniques or exercises could then be prescribed to discharge the fear until it dissipates. This is how psychoenergetics works. The techniques work amazingly well and are not difficult to do.

Let's look at another kind of problem. Suppose that you are shy and wish to be less shy. Again, there are a number of possible approaches, but one reason for shyness is the individual's unwillingness and uncertainty to let emotions flow through his or her body. Once that uncertainty is understood and psychoenergetic techniques are practiced, the individual will have less fear (though not necessarily more social skills, though social skills can be better practiced when the fear has been dissipated).

Once thoughts and behaviors can be expressed as emotional energetic relationships, they can be dealt with in a new way, one that emphasizes feeling over thinking.

All effective therapies change the emotional, mental, and spiritual energies of a person. The emotional energy model can also make some fairly good approximations about the amount of energetic exchange required to heal a particular type of dysfunction as well. The energies we create and those pushed at us, as it were, have depth and follow rules that are quite consistent.

For example, in an individual who has been repeatedly molested, we might predict that the stored energy would be difficult to expel without a very intense and powerful discharge of anger. With this individual, we would predict that intense crying, screaming, and perhaps vigorous movements might be necessary before such an intense charge could be dispelled. Our work at the Oceanview Wellness Center indicates that many types of symptoms associated with molestation can be rapidly reduced when a vigorous discharge of emotions can be achieved, even when the individual is already in a support group or other individual therapy.

THE PSYCHOENERGETIC WAY

Psychoenergetics describes the concepts and techniques that the mind uses to interact and work with emotional energies in very specific ways. It is based on a thorough understanding of the nature of the mind and the reality in which it lives. The more you understand the functions of your own mind, the more flexible you can be in solving your problems and creating the life that you desire.

Psychoenergetics, the method described in this book to solve problems and relieve stress, is based on the concept of the mind's ability to move emotional energy. As you consciously go from one thought to another, you are using your mind to "move energy" automatically. Just as your thoughts change, so do your moods. In that sense, there is nothing more difficult about moving energy than changing your mind.

Feelings Drive the Thought

Psychoenergetic principles state that feelings drive our ideas or thoughts, instead of the other way around, as is generally believed. By removing the unwanted feelings—by feeling them, not thinking about them—we can move the change process ahead phenomenally faster.

This is not to say that understanding is not important—it absolutely is. But the true *resistance* to change exists at the feeling level, not at the logical, cognitive level.

In fact, we have many feelings that we don't understand, don't know where they come from, and that are contradictory and self-destructive. However, they can still be released merely by saying and thinking certain things in a prescribed way.

Psychoenergetics works by using the basic principle that the mind can and does recognize its own truth at the deepest unconscious level. This occurs often in spite of a stated belief made by the conscious mind. When the mind hears its truth spoken out loud several times with conviction, it begins to signal that fact and sets off sensations or subtle feelings somewhere in the body.

These feelings may not initially be felt. In fact, the rule is that the mind *cannot avoid* signaling because thoughts are magnetic. Upon hearing one of its own thoughts spoken aloud, the mind resonates, much like two guitar strings playing the same note. Techniques can then be developed to amplify the feelings while simultaneously developing greater sensitivity to them—what I call *awareness* of these feelings. With sufficient awareness of your feelings, and armed with techniques to move these feeling energies, you can now move them directly and effectively.

Awareness of your feelings, then, is the sign that you are working directly with your mind and can begin to interact with and influence it. You now release the unpleasant feelings from a point within yourself to somewhere outside. But the feelings are moving not only within the mind—they are intimately connected with the body and, therefore, must be felt moving out of or through the body as well. When you release unpleasant feelings with the proper intention, you will find an amazing change not only in the way you feel but in how you think and behave as well. You don't necessarily need to understand the origin of the feeling to release it, but you must accept the destructive nature of the feeling and have the desire to let it go.

Since you release emotions physically, the more you can experience the feeling, the more relief you feel, and a greater depth of change results. By extension, it is possible to release emotions directly out of the body without going through the mind at all. Various types of body therapy often produce a great deal of release and permanent change, such as Rolfing, Feldenkrais work, and various forms of deep tissue work. (Ida Rolf developed a form of body work that is based on the belief that emotions are held in the body's connective tissues. The way to free these emotions is to open the bound tissues through rigorous massage. Moishe Feldenkrais developed a method of body work that uses a series of gentle movements to increase the individual's awareness of his or her body and retrain the nervous system to release memories that are locked in the body.)

In the chapters that follow, you'll learn various techniques to influence your mind in the way you desire. By using combinations of spoken words repeated in patterns, along with the use of images, breath, and sound, you'll be able to release unhealthy emotional energies. You will also learn much about the complexity of emotions and individual characteristics that require special understanding.

All you need now is a desire to change your life forever.

CHAPTER 2

Basic Concepts of Psychoenergetics

ENERGY AND THE MATRIX

In order to use our minds to gain mastery over our emotions, we must first understand a few basic concepts. In this section, I will cover general ideas about energies and look at how a human being is perceived from the psychoenergetic point of view. These ideas are a little different from most techniques that try to improve the way people understand their feelings. When you are finished acquainting yourself with the model presented here, you will find the exercises much easier to do.

Let's look now at a few principles that guide our efforts to achieve emotional release the psychoenergetic way.

Humans Are Energy Beings

We are composed of many types of energies. The physical part of ourselves—our bodies—consists of molecules that can be broken down into smaller units—atoms, which in turn break down into electrons and protons. These particles of mass are known to behave like waves of energy. Many experiments have shown that thought can influence these subatomic particles. So, in that sense, our bodies are all energy.

However, we appear physically solid in only one dimension. Another scientific theory holds that we consist of billions of wave-like particles, which interact with all the other energies of the universe, such as sunlight, electricity, and nuclear radiation. We even interact with feeling energies from everyone around us. Everything and everybody is in effect interacting with everything and everybody else. If you have had the experience of coming into a room and suddenly feeling a strong emotion—whether fear, sadness, or joy—it is because you are constantly sending out and being bombarded with thoughts and feelings from others, whether you know it or not. These thoughts and feelings can often change our moods, especially in a crowd.

Our Real Selves

It is clear that we are more than merely our bodies; we are just as much—if not more so—our thoughts and feelings. Most people would, in fact, identify themselves with their personalities and memories much more so than with their bodies. These thoughts can be more precisely defined as our ideas (the mental part) combined with our feelings (the emotional part) to form one unit, the *complete thought.*

An example of a complete thought is, "I don't think anyone will ever love me for who I am." This thought consists of a core idea about being loved, coupled with an implied feeling, such as doubt, fear, or concern. Another complete thought might be, "I'm confident that I can complete the goals that I set for myself"—an idea about goals combined with a feeling of confidence. The difference between the two thoughts is that the first expresses pessimism and the second expresses confidence, a positive thought. Our attention will be focused on the pessimistic or negative thoughts because it is these thoughts that tend to keep us from being happy and healthy.

These complete thought statements are not merely words; they are bundles of mental and emotional energy, much like television waves that you can't see but you know exist when you turn on the set. These statements form energy patterns that remain stable within an individual and are thought to exist simultaneously in one's mind or nonphysical self, as well as in or on the physical body itself.

To make this concept clearer, I constructed a model of how these patterns look and have placed them in a series of horizontal and vertical lines called a *grid.* In Figure 1 you will find this grid in the form of a cube.

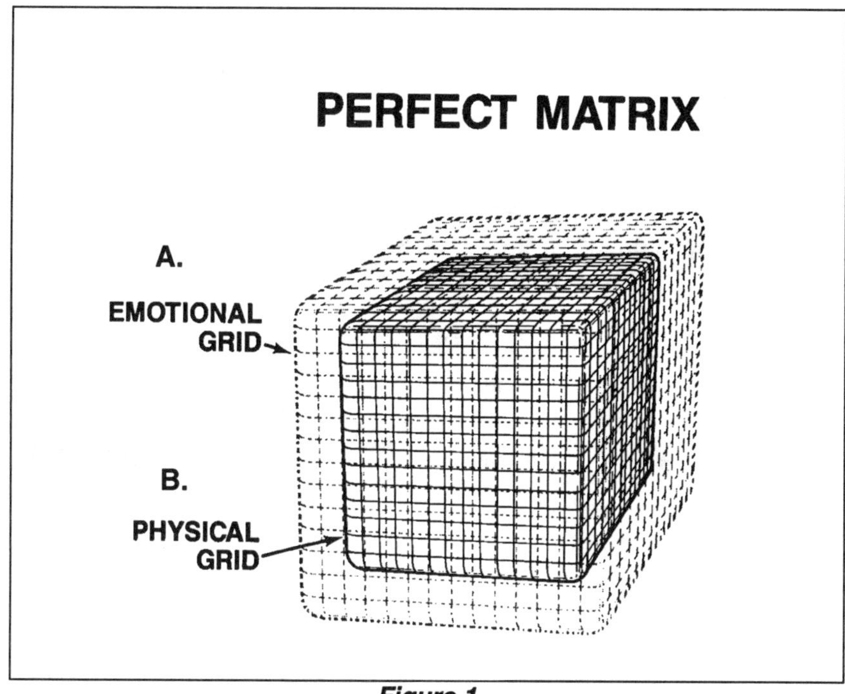

Figure 1

The previous illustration has two parts. In Part A, you see a grid composed of dotted lines, which represents the Emotional/Mental (E/M) Grid. Part B represents the Physical Grid as straight lines. When the two are overlapped, you can see what I call the Perfect Grid, or *matrix.* The matrix is perfect because there are no breaks or distortions in the grids that compose it. Of course, we know we're not without distortions, but this illustration provides a starting point for thinking about ourselves as energy beings.

Webster's dictionary defines a matrix as "something within which something else originates and develops" or, alternatively, "natural material in which something is embedded." Both definitions fit in this case because our emotional aspect originates within our physical selves, or is embedded in it. We are, as individuals, the sum total of the energy patterns as they exist within this matrix.

Therefore, we can say that a person is a matrix—a combination of flesh-and-blood energy and the sum total of all the person's emotions and thoughts. Complete thoughts, then, are the building blocks for the E/M Grid and the whole matrix. If we accept these concepts, then we can say that an emotional problem or physical disease is a matrix problem.

Of the many thousands of patterns that make up our personal philosophy, most are generally neutral or positive. We do, however, have our fair share of negative or self-defeating patterns, and these distort our otherwise perfect grid. Likewise, our physical bodies are far from perfect, and so any physical abnormality, whether it exists as a disease or a genetic potentiality, also will distort its own grid and the whole matrix as well. In Figure 2, I illustrate this more realistic view of our personal matrix, the Imperfect Mind/Body Matrix.

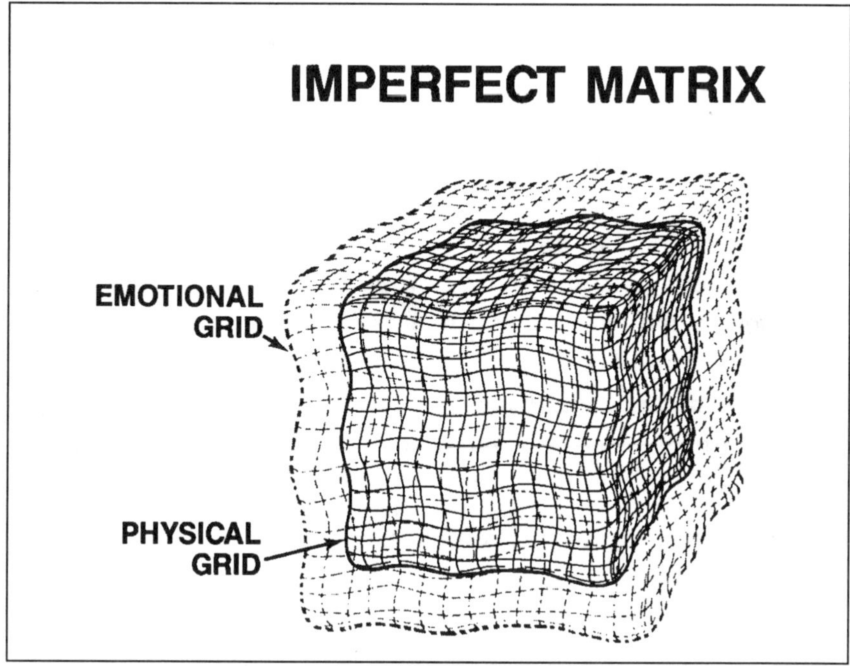

Figure 2

This Imperfect Matrix can be thought of as a three-dimensional object that is always undergoing change but is basically stable. Every day we are simultaneously growing, aging, and dying. On a day-to-day basis, however, the matrix seems fairly stable unless a major trauma occurs, such as the death of a loved one or a serious illness.

Thought patterns alone are capable of distorting the whole matrix, including the physical part, because they can contain unhealthy emotional energy. For example, we can feel unhealthy as a result of stress, which causes us to tense up, or contract, under unfavorable conditions. This is why stress management always begins with relaxation. Unhealthy energy is also unpredictable. Often when we say that we feel anxious or fearful, uncertainty is at the root of the problem.

Here is a simple exercise to illustrate how unhealthy feelings can affect you. Read the next paragraph and try to follow my instructions.

To help illustrate how unhealthy feelings such as anxiety can affect your whole matrix, think about the last time something happened to make you anxious. Maybe it was taking your driver's test, starting a new job, or the last time a loved one yelled at you. Did you feel as if things were irregularly moving around inside you and that your thoughts were jumbled and disordered? Close your eyes and think about anything that makes you anxious or worried. Notice how these thoughts make you feel. This is what I call *chaotic energy.*

Now try a simple relaxation exercise. Sit in a comfortable chair with your hands in your lap and your feet flat on the floor. Close your eyes and take a deep breath. Release it slowly with a whooshing sound. Do this two more times.

Compare how you feel at the end of the relaxation exercise with the way you felt when something anxiety-provoking happened. You will notice that in a calm state your movements, both physical and on the inside, are smoother, more regular, and predictable. Being calm means you are in a state of pleasant certainty or predictability. The more unpredictable the situation, the more chaotic the energy and the stronger the feeling. Chaos also distorts our thought patterns more and, in turn, the matrix itself. At the center we call chaotic energy *negative energy* because it tends to distort the matrix in an unhealthy way. Negative doesn't mean bad or evil, but merely is a statement about order and predictability. Other names for negative energy are *anger, fear, sorrow, pain,* and *guilt.* In addition, negative energy is not useful, in the sense that it blocks our goals and desires for happiness, health, and prosperity. The best you can say about negative energy is that it can be used to teach us what we need to do to get the things we want by moving in a more positive direction.

Stress management techniques try to bring about a state of calm, and the same is true of psychoenergetics. Together we will help you calm yourself by releasing and removing the chaotic energy that is locked in your thoughts. We want to smooth out the matrix and this work forms one of the core ideas of this book.

THREE WAYS TO DETECT FALSE PATTERNS OF FEELING

Feel your feelings. Don't *think* them.

Chaotic patterns exist in all of us, but many people don't recognize them as such. We must also keep in mind that everyone has his or her own matrix, which is always interacting at some level with those nearby. What we have, then, are many pattern-laden matrixes meeting with one another, sometimes without our being aware of what's going on. (See Figure 3 on page 16.)

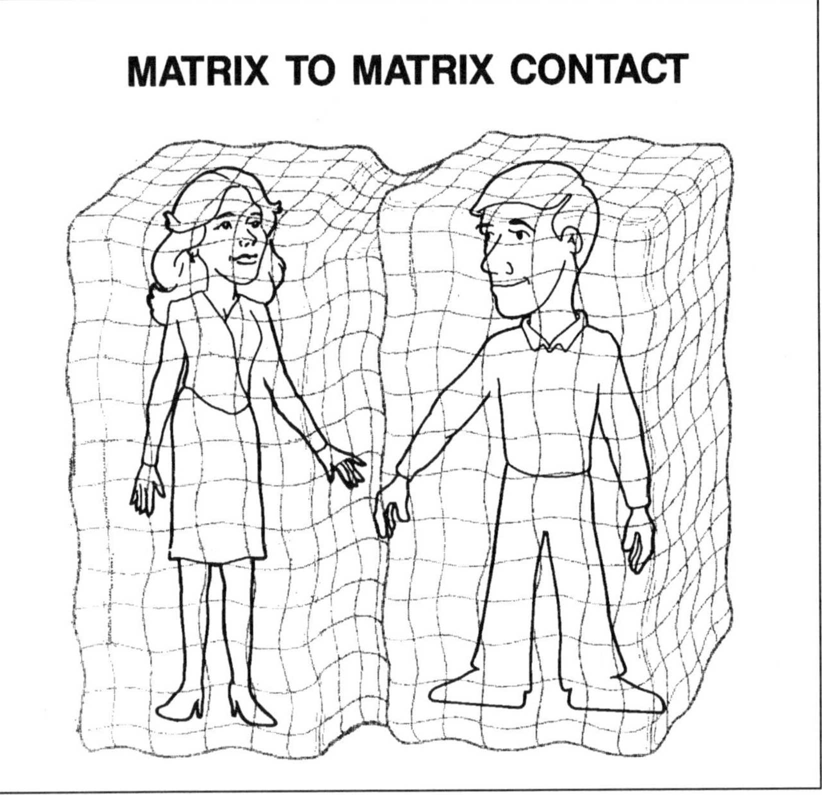

Figure 3

There are three basic ways in which these distorted patterns can be experienced first hand. The first way is by feeling your complete thoughts *directly in or on your body somewhere.* (Your ability to perceive these feelings will depend in large measure on your level of awareness of subtle feelings, a subject we will study in Chapter 6.)

For example, the phrase, "I feel unworthy to receive love," can often be felt in the chest or heart and may cause an aching or a squeezing sensation if you believe it. Likewise, a child's statement, "The kids embarrassed me at school today," can produce a stomachache or an inability to eat when the anecdote is retold at the dinner table.

To experience these subtle but very real feelings, you must be able to point your finger to the place where you feel them. For example, extend your finger from your navel up one inch and down two inches and from front to back. The feelings, then, should be thought of as having a length, height, and width. *Feeling* your feelings will take on a more precise definition than you may have ever known.

Here is an example of this method of feeling one's feelings.

Eddie, a middle-aged stockbroker on the verge of divorce, couldn't figure out why he felt so awkward when meeting new women. He was convinced it was because he was just shy and out of practice. I suggested that perhaps it wasn't quite so simple and asked him to repeat a pattern that I felt was valid for him—the phrase, "I feel guilty when I think about women in a sexual way."

Almost immediately Eddie noticed a feeling of nausea in the pit of his stomach. He was amazed that such feelings appeared because he had no conscious awareness of feeling guilty about something that he thought was natural. Had I merely suggested to him that he might feel guilty, he may well have doubted my "interpretation" and wasted valuable time solving his problem. The nauseous feelings verified that a false belief pattern existed in his matrix.

That is what is meant by *feeling your patterns* or *feeling your thoughts.* They are not merely an idea or psychological interpretation in your head. This is a crucial point and bears repeating:

Unless they are felt someplace in or on the body, feelings become merely ideas.

Words like *anger, fear,* and *love* are the names we give the movement of these feelings as they course through our bodies.

What we are experiencing are the energies of our emotions. As they move through us, they activate different tissues and organs. The subjective experience of these *energy flows* is the method by which we set sail the course of our life. It is these energy flows—the warmth in our hearts or the twist in our guts—that determine whom we shall marry, where we shall live, and what job we shall do.

Visualize Your Feelings

The second way we become aware of our patterns is through the pictures they create in our minds. The patterns, when activated, include memories of events and constructed pictures or created hypothetical possibilities ranging from the most pleasant to the most feared. Here is an example from my experience:

Dana, a fortyish housewife, had been sexually molested by her father while her mother apparently let it occur. Her complaints were chronic back pain and a failing marriage. I asked her to repeat the phrase, "I can't trust anyone not to hurt me." Immediately she was back at home cleaning for her mother at age nine. The memory was recalled in perfect detail, except that Dana had a backache at the time she was remembering.

In this case, the words brought to mind both pictures and feelings. Another way to verify that a pattern is correct for you is by the pictures that spontaneously arise when the pattern is repeated. Sometimes feelings immediately appear; other times, only a picture. Either way, pictures are a way to detect patterns of feelings.

Feelings As Communication

Patterns exist as bits of dialogue that come as a result of inner communication in which the conscious self speaks to the unconscious and asks a question and receives a pattern.

Jenny came to me because of an abusive marriage that she knew was bad for her, but she couldn't figure out why she resisted leaving. I asked her to ask her inner self, "Why don't you let me leave this crazy man?" Her mind responded, "You'll die without a man, and you know it." I asked her to repeat these phrases, and she began to cry and cough.

Using Your Unconscious Mind

The third and often most direct way to cause patterns to appear is to ask your unconscious mind for information about the problems you are addressing. Generally, when it speaks, it reveals a useful pattern that can be repeated aloud to generate a powerful feeling. In Chapter 9, I will discuss in-depth the techniques necessary to wring the truth from your unconscious mind.

Simple one-line statements of truth, such as "I can't trust anyone not to hurt me," are the building blocks of who we are in terms of our personality, feelings, and behaviors. We organize our inner and, from there, our outer world with complete thought patterns. Everything we feel and see, our opinions and philosophy of life, can be broken down to one-sentence statements. The amount of feeling contained in these one-liners is easy to underestimate. One of the main points of this book is to help you find these powerful statements and use them to your benefit.

Ultimately, as you develop the ability to more accurately discern your patterns, an infinite number of techniques become available for healing and transformation. For you are now at the very energetic core of your being, unobstructed by theories and speculations about human behavior. Know that every aspect of your life—memories, feelings, ideas and behaviors, all that you know and do—can be described as a part of an energetic pattern.

CHAPTER 3

BELIEFS AND BLOCKS

In the previous chapter, we discussed the concept of a complete thought—a thought that contains both a mental portion, or pure idea, and an emotional, or feeling part. In theory, no thought can be purely mental or purely emotional. Even mathematical formulas may not be free of feelings because they are connected to memories that are associated with feeling situations. For example, if your first association with math was going up to the blackboard and hearing the class laugh when you got the answer wrong or applaud you when you got it right, even simple addition may have complex emotions attached to it.

Likewise, there are no purely emotional states without idea content, although intense physical pain, sexual ecstasy, or ecstatic religious experiences might come close. By realizing that your thoughts are two-dimensional, you can better understand the concepts that will be presented in this chapter.

CONCEPT OF A COMPLETE THOUGHT

Imagine that a complete thought looks like the illustration in Figure 4.

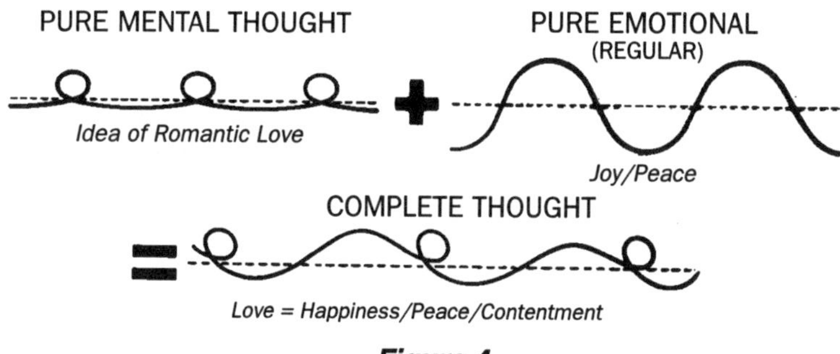

Figure 4

The mental portion of the thought is represented by small, even circles, and the emotion is depicted with large, regular waves. The lower portion shows the complete thought as consisting of even circles combined with regular waves. This illustration might be of a person's feelings of joy and calm in romantic love.

By contrast, in Figure 5, we have a mental thought paired with the chaotic feelings of pain and loss, which are pictured as lines without form or order. The combined, complete thought

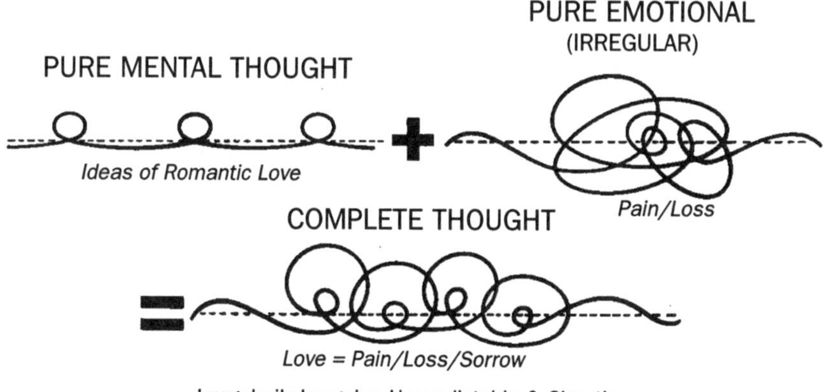

Figure 5

is conceptualized as irregular and would be experienced as an anxious unpleasant feeling.

In Figure 6 we have removed a portion of the emotional content from the complete thought. When this is done, a curious thing happens; the underlying complete pattern changes, and the individual feels differently *regardless of whether or not he or she understands why or how this occurred.*

COMPLETE THOUGHT

Released Chaotic Energy

Figure 6

Here are examples from my experiences:

Daniela came to me because she had always been afraid of escalators, though she had no idea why. I told her that we could cure her in a few sessions. I suggested she simply acknowledge the fear and use a few simple patterns to remove the fear energy. She acknowledged and released her fear about getting caught in the escalator and was able to overcome her fear. When there is little reinforcement for keeping irrational fears, they often disappear rather easily.

Candy came to see me because of stress at work. She felt overworked and harassed by her employer and eventually had to leave the job. Initially, she was depressed and somewhat anxious. Soon after quitting, though, she began to experience panic while driving on freeways. She would have to pull off the road because she felt as if she were going to have a heart attack and die. Candy eventually stopped driving the freeways. She couldn't understand what the problem had to do with work stress.

I gave Candy three patterns to work on—one dealing with anger at her boss for harassing her, a second for anger at herself for letting him do it, and a third simply to acknowledge the fear that she would die on the freeway. By working and releasing these patterns without knowing why one led to the other, she was able to correct the problem and returned to driving in a few weeks.

The overemphasis on the mental component to the detriment of the emotional component is, I think, one of the weaknesses of traditional psychotherapy. The enormous power of emotion to motivate our behavior is not yet fully appreciated. Therefore, little time is spent on adequate techniques to release this hidden and very powerful element. Psychoenergetics focuses on emotional energies as the primary avenue for life change, and the two-part, complete thought makes this possible.

The significance of the complete thought is that it allows us to change our behavior and our thought patterns in a way that is not based on how or why a pattern came into existence.

Thus, instead of trying to figure out why you have low self-esteem, when it started, and who is responsible, we will take a more holistic approach and see the self-esteem idea as more of an energy imbalance, much like an overactive thyroid or a swollen joint. This is an entirely new way to solve problems and, in a sense, is more like a physical treatment than a psychological one.

TRUE AND FALSE BELIEFS

Complete thought patterns can be divided into two categories of beliefs: basically false or basically true. A belief is simply a category of complete thoughts that describes one's opinions on how life works. (I talk more about beliefs in Chapters 10 and 11.) They are the building blocks of one's personal philosophy. A false belief (pattern) is defined as a pattern that does not serve the individual to maintain it within his or her matrix because it inhibits the person from maximizing health and happiness. It is also energetically defined as those thought patterns that restrict or inhibit the *maximal energy flow* of that particular person. Each individual has a theoretical optimal perfect flow that promotes health and happiness.

In situations of importance, generally there are a number of choices, one being better than others. That better choice represents a more optimum (energetic) flow. A false belief (minimal energy flow) is not judged in terms of right or wrong behavior.

A true belief (pattern) is defined as what serves a person best and promotes the flow. In real-life situations, the vast majority of times, this *better* or *best* possibility can be ascertained. To do this, we must know our unconscious mind so as not to create conflict with our conscious mind. We must also know the "laws" of the mind and how emotional energies work within it.

Many of the exercises that follow address ways to be reasonably certain what energetically promotes the best, most perfect flow on issues in which you have a strong emotional interest. The emotional attachment makes the healing and transformation techniques possible.

A QUICK SUMMARY

We can summarize the ideas presented in this chapter in this way:

1. There are intrinsic thought patterns for each person that enhance and optimize his or her energy flow.
2. We call these optimum flow patterns *true* beliefs and the obstructive and limiting ones *false* beliefs.
3. We call limiting, false belief patterns *chaotic* and irregular.

4. We call chaotic, irregular energy *negative* and equivalent to anger, fear, sadness, and guilt.

By extension, anger, fear, guilt, and sadness are harmful in some way—at least in the sense that they limit optimal flow, health, happiness, and ultimately distort our matrix.

Common sense tells us that angry, fearful people are not as happy or healthy as those who are loving and have a positive attitude. Everyone knows someone whose bad attitude or pessimism robs him or her of the joy of life. In that sense, I am only confirming what you already know experientially as well as intuitively. The part that is not so obvious or intuitive is how much negative energy lies dormant—though it's a very significant factor in inhibiting our well-being.

THE STRUCTURE OF AN EMOTIONAL BLOCK

Even though false and true are not connected to right or wrong in a traditional sense, that does not mean there are no rules. There is one very important rule that we must all apply:

It should not be necessary, nor is it desirable, to block the optimizing flow of any other individual any more than you would to yourself. Any attempt to do so will eventually lead to a block within the blocking individual, leading to loss of one's own health and happiness.

Figure 7 represents the basic structure of an emotional block. We can think of a single pattern as a block, but generally, more than one (several or even dozens) combine to make a block that really affects us.

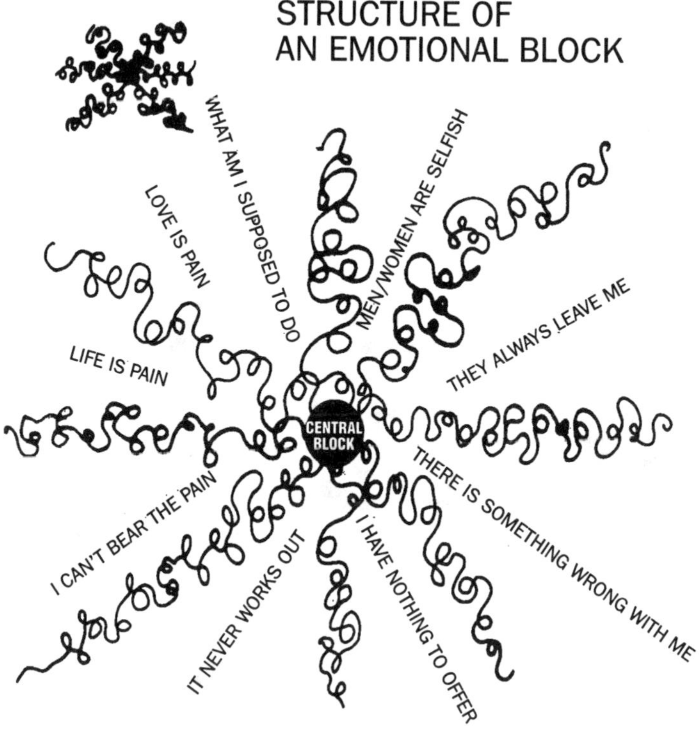

Figure 7

The block is emotional in that it prohibits us from taking advantage of (blocks) life's opportunities because of the operative beliefs. A block is also physical, in the sense that the portion of the body where the patterns are stored will be sore when touched and even painful. The release of blocks is conceptualized in Figure 8 on page 28.

The result of these patterns is that individuals who have them will never feel good enough about themselves or others to receive love. They will always feel insecure and unloved, no matter how hard they try. Even if someone really does love them, they will always doubt it. In domino fashion, this lack of self-esteem and insecurity will manifest, for example, as depression, anxiety, psychosomatic illness, chronic pain, or the pervasive sense that everyone else is better than the insecure person. It may lead him or her to unnecessary competitiveness and create a drive to succeed in order to prove that he or she is somebody.

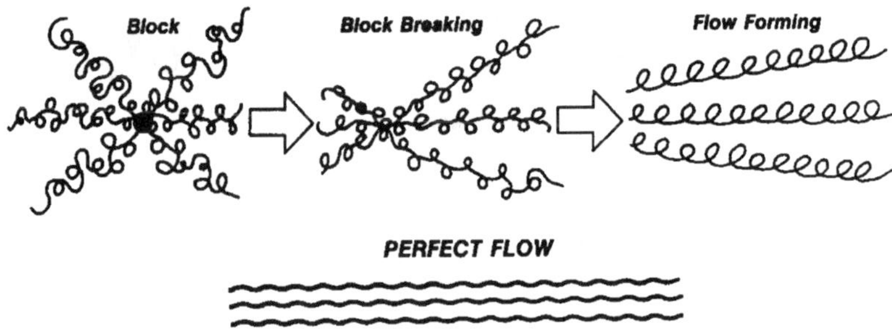
INDIVIDUAL PATTERN DOES HARM BY FORMING
A BLOCK WITH ANOTHER SIMILAR CHAOTIC PATTERN
Block
Block Breaking
Flow Forming
PERFECT FLOW
IN ORDER TO PULL THEM APART
SOME OF THE CHAOTIC "NEGATIVE" ENERGIES MUST BE RELEASED

Figure 8

THE BOTTOM LINE

When we make changes in our attitudes, our bodies open up and we realize we aren't mixed up or worthless but that somehow we got our lines crossed. When they get uncrossed, we feel a whole lot better.

Let us now begin, in earnest, our study of psychoenergetics, starting with some preparatory exercises. These will increase your sensitivity to your feelings and help to develop your overall awareness of the mind-body connection.

CHAPTER 4

REFLECTION AND MAGNETISM

In later chapters you will learn many techniques for greater awareness, ways to discover your true feelings, and how to release the negative emotions from your body/mind. This is only the beginning, for there are many levels of awareness yet to be developed and many new ways to clear your matrix.

This chapter deals with the broader implications of understanding your body/mind as you relate to others, as opposed to thinking and feeling within yourself. Human beings, as individuals, are a multiplicity of energy systems, all interacting with their environment and, more importantly, the people in their environment.

We can look more indirectly at ourselves by observing some of our behaviors as they create our interests, hobbies, friendships, and occupations. Let us now look at how such an expanded view can add to your healing—by studying magnetism and reflection. Magnetism and reflection are two ways in which the mind works fairly consistently in all human beings.

REFLECTION

In physics, when something is reflected, light waves or particles are striking a surface and coming back at the same angle as they entered. In terms of the mind, when I speak of reflections, I'm talking about something that is a true representation of what has just "bounced" off of it—that is, there are no distortions in what you are seeing. When I speak of reflections from your mind, I mean that the life you see on the outside—real life—is an accurate reflection, with no distortion, of what is inside.

For example, if deep down inside you feel unworthy of love, then your life reflection will be a life without love. Likewise, if you're kindly and loving inside, your real life should reflect a nice group of family and friends. If you think that it should be happening and it is not, you must search inside for the answers because, by definition, the reflection is accurate and without distortion.

The way to change the outside, then, is to change the inside—yourself deep down inside. As long as the outside doesn't meet your needs, you have to keep working and refining the inside. That doesn't mean there is nothing to be done on the outside. I believe that the life you lead is a pretty accurate reflection of your inner mind. If you look at your life honestly, you will know that in a reasonably straightforward way, your life is showing you what you think and believe and, therefore, what needs to be changed.

What specifically are these reflections? They are your house, car, friends, family, job—anything and everything that you choose. And because you chose them, they represent and reflect your inner tastes and preferences, your beliefs and desires.

Not every reflection you see can be changed—race, for example. So what can you change? Your lifestyle, habits, and personality. Changing these things is much less difficult than you think, especially when you consider how much you know already about reflections. You already know, for example, that the cause of a heart attack is rarely a mystery; it reflects cholesterol level, blood pressure, and stresses, among other things. The reflection is accurate; your inside metabolism is the deciding factor, not how you look on the outside. You accept this as true, so when someone suddenly dies of a heart attack, you are more likely to inquire about his stress level, blood pressure, or oat bran intake.

Just as cholesterol and salt make up your inside body, your beliefs and desires make up your personality—your character. So if you wish to make your emotional heart healthier, instead of changing cereals in the morning, you must change your beliefs.

With this new perspective, let's look at a very common reflection, one that shows you without the committed, loving relationship that you desire. On the outside, all looks fine to you; you are doing everything possible to make something happen, and you see no reason why you're not getting what you want. If, however, you were to test yourself using the awareness techniques in this book, you would discover several things.

You would learn that you have conflicting beliefs about a successful love relationship. You would find you are either fearful of a committed relationship or don't feel for some reason that you deserve one. You would also find beliefs about love as pain, loss, or submission. We could speculate that these beliefs came from early childhood experiences of which you may have no precise memories. These lost memories and feelings might reveal the awareness that, in fact, what you are most comfortable with is the opposite of what you say you truly believe and desire.

To understand how life events that happened long ago can continue to exert their influence, we need to understand what happens in one of a series of traumatic events. Small or large events that involve a lot of negative feelings tend to deform the energy grid in a significant way.

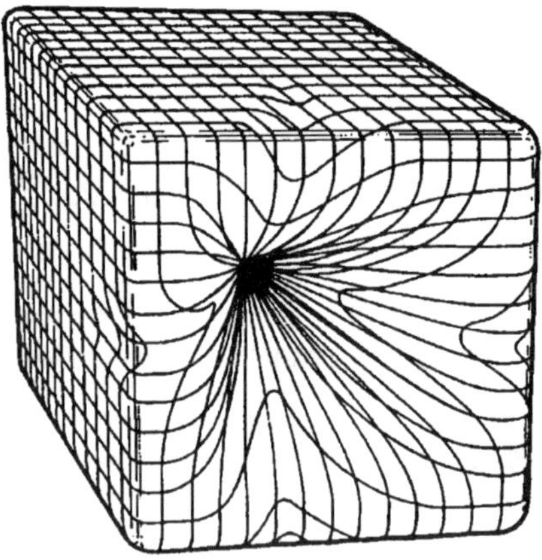

Figure 9

Picture your energy grid (see Figure 1 in Chapter 2) as a cube made of chicken wire. Powerful feelings act like a strong wind that deform the cube. Though it retains its basic shape, the stronger the emotion, the more the cube is deformed (see Figure 9). The wire is too rigid to relax back into its original shape after the wind stops, so it remains in the distorted position unless something is done to repair it. The distorted grid has been left with false belief patterns.

In a traumatized or injured individual, there may be hundreds of points on the cube that show these distortions. In the physical body, these points can show up as tender spots, especially in your chest. In a deeply traumatized person, they are deeper and harder to smooth out.

Time passes and the events that have taken place tend to be forgotten. An individual who adjusts to the new, deformed shape might be aware of this but not realize how strong the pattern of unworthiness, fear, or guilt can be. As proof of this fact, we have no better example than the fairly recent recognition in the United States (and perhaps around the world) of long-hidden physical and sexual abuse.

People are beginning to describe abusive events that occurred 30 to 40 years ago, some related to sexual abuse and some to many different problems. These people are finally figuring out the reasons for their problems. As they start to recall the events in detail, their stability is rocked, and the anger and shame are starting to bubble up after many years of apparent calm.

We also know from war veterans, especially from the Vietnam War, that an experience may be so intense that a person seemingly cannot recover—at least with the traditional talking therapies practiced today. The veteran and the abused may seem very different, but we now know that the intensity of emotion involved has created something we call Post-Traumatic Stress Disorder, the resultant symptoms of one or more intense emotional experiences (traumas) felt to be beyond the normal range a human being is expected to reasonably tolerate.

If you have been intruded upon emotionally, by continuous assault on your heart and mind with the intent of destroying your life spirit, this too is a trauma, and the patterns are deeply entrenched and create circumstances that sometimes seem to defy logic.

Only recently have these facts been recognized for their importance in human life by both the lay public and the therapeutic community. With that realization came better diagnostic and therapeutic methods to deal with these stress disorders.

What's Been Reflected Here?

We find an interesting—and common—phenomenon among victims of abuse. These individuals often have problems not with relationships, as one might expect, but with eating disorders, addictions, chronic pains, and diseases that seem unrelated to the events that caused the trauma. It is well known that abuse is so traumatic that the victims create all kinds of seemingly unrelated patterns in order to cope. Now we've also come to know that many types of problems, such as addictions and eating disorders, reflect something much deeper than what was previously supposed.

Each individual takes in the same events differently, determined by one's internal patterns. It is difficult—if not impossible—to predict exactly how any one person will react to a traumatic experience and, therefore, to predict how it will manifest in reflection. We must view these diseases as reflections of a deep pain, perhaps long forgotten consciously but nonetheless still present. For example, addictions wherein one needs continuously to deny and avoid the realities of life through drink or drugs reflects a deeper pain that must be looked for; simplistic answers like an out-of-control habit or a character flaw don't explain the behavior.

There is, then, ample evidence that the reflections you see in your life are valid and true. Although they may not seem right, fair, or possible, it is only because one does not understand the true power of the body/mind to take in and store emotional pain.

THE SPLIT

The contradiction between the observed reality and one's desires and expectations results from the false idea that our conscious mind (the outside view) and unconscious mind (the inside view) are communicating very well or are largely in agreement. The truth is probably that they are not—in fact, they may be in complete disagreement. This unconscious-conscious split leads us to perceive the opposite of our best efforts.

Another way to view the unconscious-conscious split is to use the analogy of the eye. Technically speaking, you don't see with your eyes; they are only the lenses. The interpretation of what you see is performed by the occipital lobes of the brain. Your conscious mind, like the eye, takes in the circumstances at hand but doesn't make any decisions; it merely keeps you apprised of the situation to prevent you from bumping into the furniture, so to speak. Your life is interpreted, analyzed, and configured through your unconscious mind.

If you accept that your conscious mind is the lens and not the brain, you are likely to be surprised at what is happening to you, even though you may have believed you were in control of events in your life and the decisions that preceded them. So, if you don't actually know your unconscious beliefs, you may tend to believe that the reflection that you see is inaccurate and may even be the opposite of what you desired and expected.

CHANGING YOUR REFLECTIONS

If any reflection in your life is not to your liking, decide what you want and then do the work necessary to find the source of the reflection. You need to know the truth. To know your truth, you must make contact with this all-seeing and knowing unconscious mind. If your life lacks trust, loyalty, companionship, prosperity—whatever you desire from others—you must first search within yourself. Only when you discover it inside yourself can you expect the world to respond in kind.

This holds true not only for individuals, but also for groups of people; even whole nations can be seen by their reflections. Whatever you see on the outside represents a deeper, more real truth that exists within. All you have to do is figure out how to interpret the reflections that you see to begin to make the changes you desire. I recognize that it will take much practice and experience to do so effectively. If you can do it, your efforts will be rewarded, because once again you will know what direction to take to solve very complex life problems.

You are now ready to ask yourself an important question: If it is true that your reflections represent deep unconscious beliefs of which you are generally unaware, how is it that you find yourself with the people and in the situations that you do? How do abusers find other abusers? Alcoholics other alcoholics? What mechanism inside you attracts people and events that you swear you don't really want? For this answer you must now turn to the second principle, *magnetism*.

MAGNETISM

Magnetism is, I believe, an explanation for all that you see. For example, look at the widely-held notion that opposites attract. You can see such different personalities in couples that it seems as if they are opposites. On the outside perhaps, but on the inside they are more alike than you might expect.

Once again, this is a case of outside appearances as opposed to inside beliefs. A common pairing of couples would be the dramatic, emotional wife with the seemingly unemotional, rather mental husband. This supposedly unfeeling man is an illusion. In reality he has the same deep feelings as anyone else but is unable to express them. In fact, he finds emotional women attractive enough to marry someone who is his "opposite." Likewise, his mate, allegedly short on thinking and long on feeling, is equally attracted to his type and often hides her true self as well.

All of this is happening because our beliefs are magnetic, somewhat like the attraction between certain metals, but in a nonphysical way. These magnetic beliefs make people like radar, each broadcasting some of their strongest signals (beliefs) and each attracted to (receiving) a signal much like their own. This magnetism tends to draw not only people but also life experiences that are consistent with one's beliefs.

Because you are the product of thousands of beliefs, your life is the sum total of all these forces pulling together. So it is possible to go inside to change the outside because, as human beings, we operate on the magnetism principle. If you change the kinds of things that you attract and are attracted to, you will in effect have a different life. You will find someone attractive who activates your hidden magnetic beliefs, even if that is not your intention. You cannot help yourself until you know these beliefs are operative and how to change them.

The best example of this is how adults who were abused as children—especially women—manage to find sexually abusing husbands as fathers for their children without a word being spoken about the subject. Perhaps these women are unaware consciously of what happened to them. If this mismatch of abused with abusers were an occasional event, we might call it a coincidence, but it is very common. We might speculate that the man read the woman's body language, or saw some vulnerability in her eyes. In fact, the men themselves rarely plan to be attracted to these women on a conscious level.

People have electromagnetic energy patterns not unlike radios or televisions. These patterns have a frequency much like a musical chord. The notes in the chord resonate with one another. In effect, we are always in or out of resonance with the people around us. It is common to feel close to someone you've known for a very short period of time, even feeling closer than to someone you have known for years.

Conversely, it is possible to instantly dislike someone. Those whom we dislike are excellent examples of reflections worth studying hard, because if we are insightful enough to recognize our reaction as irrational, we can find some helpful patterns that we might have missed otherwise.

Look at another example of magnetism at work in your daily life: the jobs you choose. Careers and jobs are very magnetic at a deeply unconscious level. Magnetism probably has more to do with career choice than intelligence or aptitude. It is often jokingly said that psychiatrists choose to work with emotionally troubled people so that they can work on their own problems. This is more often true than false. Psychiatrists as a group are very thoughtful, introspective people who wish to know what makes them tick. They are attracted to figuring out other people in the hopes of understanding themselves. They are interested in the mental process, so they are attracted to others who are trying to do the same.

When the principle of magnetism and the reflections generated are understood, many of society's problems will be more easily solved.

A belief is a relative thing; one can believe 1% or 99% in something. The percentage directly reflects the intensity or power of the magnetic pull behind it. The existence of even a small percentage of belief means that it exists as a potential. This potential means you may be attracted to or draw to you persons or situations that may completely surprise you.

The more you work with and come to accept deep belief systems as magnetic entities, the more you will be in control of your life and feel you are not subject to the whims of fate and chance. This is an empowering experience, but it also means accepting a higher level of personal responsibility for the events in your life.

MAGNETIC BELIEFS AND HEALING

The magnetism property has both disadvantages and advantages. The major disadvantage is that it operates whether or not you want it to. This means that events appear out of control for many, and undesirable reflections appear again and again. In addition, the pull of magnetism is very strong, and sheer willpower may not be enough to overcome it. Witness the difficulty experienced with alcoholism and drug addiction, for example.

The major advantage is that these same magnetic properties facilitate their own discovery and release, so that when you understand the principle and can read the reflections correctly, it becomes much easier to change yourself without the struggle and resistance that often accompanies attempts at life changes. This ease of removal is seen in the simplicity of the technique to activate and release false belief patterns. Thus, the very act of repeating them silently or aloud automatically stimulates them, making them vulnerable to being removed.

When you are certain about what you want removed, it becomes relatively easy to magnetize the ones you don't want and ask your mind to help release them. This is the basic principle of pattern removal—*activation* and *release*. Because the beliefs are magnetic, it is possible to remove them without knowing exactly where they came from. Once the pull is gone, the struggle is gone too.

There are natural laws that govern the mind and its relationship to the body, and if these are followed, certain predictable events will occur. Knowing your true mind and feeling your thoughts is essential to accurately determining what you wish to remove magnetically and how much is actually there to be removed. Your feelings and associated images are constantly giving you feedback about how you are doing and how much of a given belief is still operative.

The magnetic principle of beliefs has implications for many life events and relationships not detailed here. The study of the nature of magnetic beliefs goes far beyond what can be given in a few pages; it is a course of study in itself. My purpose in this book is to give you the basic system for restructuring human behavior. If you learn to feel your thoughts and experience magnetism, then you have gone far beyond most people, and I promise you will gain greater insights into the hows and whys of the world around you.

PRACTICE WITH REFLECTIONS

Take a few moments now to think about some aspects of your life—your friends, family, job, and personal possessions. Next make a note of the beliefs that governed your choices. Always strive to delve more deeply for the reasons underlying those choices. Do not be satisfied with such answers as "I just did" or "I just liked it." Never accept the answer "I don't know." Make up something, and then see if it strikes you as the truth. If it doesn't, try another answer. In order to understand your reflections, you must study them and become a skilled observer.

Beliefs about JOB

Example: *I'm not smart enough to be an X, so I'll just be a Y.*

1. I believe this because I didn't finish college.

2. I believe this because . . .

Beliefs about SPOUSE

Example: *I'm unable to run my own life, so I'd better find someone who will tell me what to do.*

1. I believe this because decisions I've made for myself don't turn out well.

2. I believe this because . . .

Beliefs about CAR, HOUSE, FRIENDS

Example: *If I have this car (friend, house, etc.), people will think I am somebody special.*

1. I believe this because I'm impressed by people who have an expensive car (house, important friend).

2. I believe this because . . .

PRACTICE WITH MAGNETISM

Begin to notice what attracts you and what repels you—whether it is people, situations, or even objects, especially when there is no apparent basis for it. For example, you meet a man for the first time and take an immediate like/dislike to him. Try to describe, as accurately as you can, what parts are attractive and what parts are repulsive. If you make an effort, you will find you have a definite feeling about almost everything in your world. You have always had this ability, but you probably never attempted to verbalize it before.

As you practice these skills, you will find that you are learning more and more about how you really think and feel deep down inside. Awareness of your deep feelings is the first step in the process of removing patterns that cause unwanted behaviors and life situations.

CHAPTER 5

BREATHING

Of all the bodily functions, none is more important than breathing—the pursuit of oxygen. Deprived of oxygen for as little as two or three minutes, the brain will leave a healthy body without direction. The sensation of being breathless—unable to take in air or let it out—is one of the most frightening experiences we can have.

Conversely, the feeling of breathing deeply and easily with your body relaxed is one of the most pleasurable sensations you can experience, though you are seldom conscious of it.

However, as normal and natural as breathing seems to be, it is done inefficiently and incorrectly for the most part. Considering that the average person doesn't fully benefit from his or her breathing, the first step to facilitate healing is to learn the hows and whys of proper breathing.

CHECKING YOUR EQUIPMENT

Breathing begins with actively inhaling slowly—preferably through the nasal passages—bringing air deep into the lungs. This process lowers and contracts the diaphragm, a powerful muscle about two inches thick at the bottom of the lungs which separates the chest from the abdominal cavity. In proper breathing, the abdomen extends out, reaches a peak, and then, like a balloon, releases air from the belly. As the air is exhaled, usually through the nose, the abdomen naturally shrinks back to its normal size. Any blockage in the inflow or outflow of air will result in decreased vigor.

The nasal passages need to be maximally open to achieve proper breathing, and the lungs should expand without pain or discomfort to efficiently absorb air and release it easily. The diaphragm must be loose and easily expanded; the abdomen must also be able to comfortably expand without obstruction or discomfort.

Take a moment now to notice how easily air flows into your nose. Does the air go in through both nostrils or only one? Put your finger over one nostril and close it off. See how it feels to breathe with one nostril and then the other. Recent research indicates that your nostrils alternate between open and closed every 1-3/4 hours throughout the day, so don't be concerned if only one nostril is open. If, however, chronic nasal congestion is a problem, you may need to consult an ear, nose, and throat specialist or an allergist. You may also elect to use nutritional supplements and diet to deal with allergies; there are many books available on this subject.

Your breathing equipment also includes your lungs and chest wall. Broken ribs or deformities may impair breathing by mechanical obstruction; scarred, diseased, or aged lungs may expand little and make inhaling or exhaling difficult. If you have such problems, consultation with your physician or lung specialist may be of value. The diaphragm, though rarely injured or damaged, may be so underexercised that it is effectively dormant and may take some effort to wake up. With a little practice, it will become flexible again soon.

Finally, in order to take deep breaths, the abdomen must be able to expand freely. It too may be tight because of tension or chronic inactivity. Today's emphasis on beauty, fitness, and flat stomachs makes some people reluctant to relax their abdomen.

Nevertheless, with very little effort, the abdomen can be trained to expand freely to achieve the deepest breaths. As you will come to see, developing an awareness of a body part or mental process is often enough to cause it to change.

BREATHING AND ENERGY RELEASE

Breathing can be tight or constricted when there is conflict or confusion about important emotional issues. The tendency for breath to "stick" is itself a block and represents other blocks as well. The tightening or intermittent opening and constriction occurs in response to emotionally charged thoughts that the mind would prefer not to think too much about.

The first order of business, then, is to make sure that you are physically able to follow the exercises in this chapter. If you are not, you may need to experiment to find ways of compensating so you can gain accurate feedback when doing the various techniques.

Assuming you are in good health, as you open up to deep breaths, you will find a release of nonspecific tension. First, and more importantly, you will feel more. The more you feel, the better you will be able to interpret your feedback, and the more easily you will be able to release blocked emotions.

Inhalation

Inhalation is best accomplished through the nose, which warms the air and filters dirt from it. As you inhale, remember to fill your abdomen first and then, little by little, fill your lungs until you feel the air reaching the level of your shoulders, which will rise as you inhale.

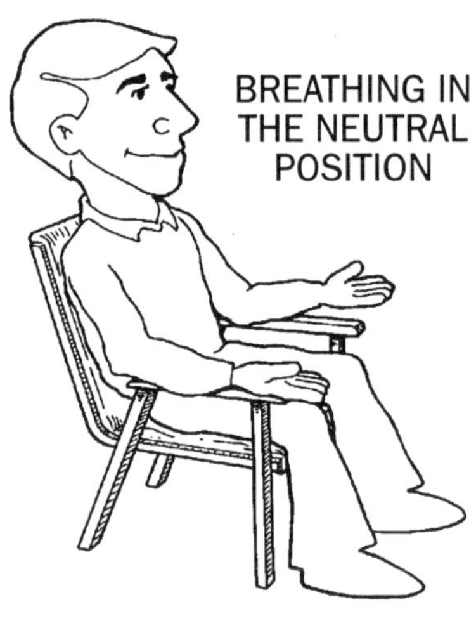
BREATHING IN
THE NEUTRAL
POSITION

Figure 10A

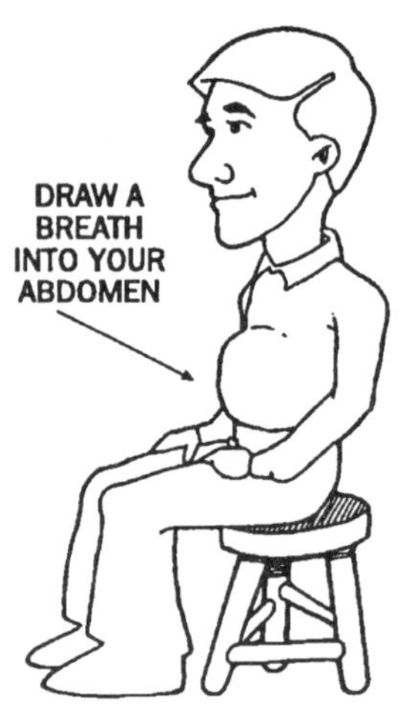
DRAW A
BREATH
INTO YOUR
ABDOMEN

Figure 10B

Breathing correctly with your back straight and arms at your sides is called *breathing in the neutral position* (see Figure 10A). This may feel a little uncomfortable at first, but it will start to feel good very soon. Breathing should be pleasurable. Each breath you take should add to your health. As you expand your breathing capacities, you'll be more efficient, needing to breathe less and using less energy while taking in more oxygen. Upper-chest breathing is anxiety-producing, and as you learn to avoid it, you'll find that you're calmer and able to last longer on the "hold," the next step.

To inhale properly, sit upright in a comfortable chair in the neutral position. With your arms at your sides or in your lap, slowly draw a breath into your belly. Make your abdomen swell out, and fill it as much as you can for a few seconds (see Figure 10B). Now let the breath out. Repeat this three or four more times.

This manner of breathing may seem strange at first, and you might not be able to fill your belly every time. Practice by placing your hand—or, better yet, someone else's hand—on your belly. Feel the pressure inside, and try to resist that pressure with your hand.

After you've succeeded in puffing out your abdomen a few times, take a deep breath and this time first fill your belly and then your lungs. It might help to picture the air filling you from the bottom of your belly to the top of your shoulders. By the time you have finished inhaling this deep breath, your shoulders should have moved upward and outward. Try this a few more times. We'll return to this exercise later.

The Hold

Holding your breath serves several purposes. One is to take in more oxygen, which feels good and nourishes the tissues. The second is to increase the amount of carbon dioxide in your blood stream. This has a calming effect and is one of nature's more effective anti-anxiety agents. This is the rationale behind having someone breathe into a paper bag when he or she gets extremely anxious or is hyperventilating.

A third reason for holding your breath is that the air itself contains what I call *life force.* In a sense, this life force is everywhere, but it is most accessible through breathing. The life force is absorbed much like oxygen, through the breath-holding process. As you do the exercises in this chapter, you will feel yourself becoming more energized with each breath.

Exhaling

The proper way to exhale under most circumstances is to breathe out through the nose. However, energy releasing, which is our purpose here, is not normal breathing; therefore, we need to look at specific ways to breathe out to promote the release of feelings.

The exhaled breath can be held in the mouth, giving additional power and accuracy to your imagery. This is done by pursing your lips and blowing out, as if through a straw. Take a breath and blow gently as if you were blowing slowly through a straw. Can you feel how directed and precise it feels? In this way your images and breathing can be coordinated to give you maximum benefit.

Take a couple of minutes now to practice exhaling as described in the next exercise. Remember that the idea is to hold your breath without hurting yourself or turning blue.

BEGINNING BREATHING EXERCISES

Exercise 1: Exhaling Through a Straw

Controlled exhalation allows you to visualize and breathe in a coordinated fashion giving your breath greater power. In the martial arts, such as judo and karate, breath control is emphasized as a way to increase your power and quiet your mind. After controlled exhalation, it's easy to go into a meditative state, if you desire.

Let's inhale for four counts, hold for four counts, and exhale for six counts. (A count is basically one heart beat.) Remember, as you exhale, to purse your lips as if you are blowing through a straw or, if you prefer, into someone's ear. When you're finished, try this two more times. Count slowly.

Now sit back for a moment, close your eyes, and feel it. Can you see why breath control is so valuable? The cleansing sensation is enhanced when you know what you are blowing out along with the air, such as uncomfortable feelings. The next set of exercises will show you how to free your emotions as you breathe.

Now let's focus attention on how you can use breathing to your advantage the psychoenergetic way.

Exercise 2: Freeing Emotions Through Deep Inhalation

If you found, while doing an inventory of your breathing apparatus, that your diaphragm is rigid and tight, you'll need to do some stretching exercises. A "stuck" diaphragm tends to hold in feelings; stretching can help you gain access to whatever emotion is bothering you. Begin this way:

Wherever you are, sit in a comfortable position. First, increase the depth of your inhalation, slowly breathing in for the count of four to six. Puff out your abdomen as much as you can. It's going to feel funny, but that is to be expected. You may have to practice for at least four to five days with some regularity before you begin to notice that you have more flexibility. Then you'll be ready to increase the length of inhalation, working your way to 8 or even 16 counts, and talking to yourself about your feelings.

Now inhale for six or more counts and say to yourself silently:

> *"I am opening up to allow my feelings of anger to surface."*

As you breathe in, repeat the phrase five or six times, or for as long as you're taking in air. Do this even if you don't think that you are angry or don't feel anything during the exercise. Simply think of it as practice for a time when you *do* need to release anger. Breathe, stretching your diaphragm, and repeat the phrase over and over for five more breaths. Take a moment to sense how you feel. Be aware of feeling agitated or tense in any way.

When you inhale slowly from 4 to 12 counts, silently say the next phrase:

> *"I am opening up to allow my feelings of fear to surface."*

Once again, even if you're not fearful at this moment, consider this as preparation, and repeat it throughout the breaths for five or six times. Take at least a minute to process what you have done, and note the slightest changes in your feelings. Then say the third phrase:

> *"I am opening up to allow my feelings of sadness to surface."*

Take time to process the feelings that may have surfaced and continue breathing. Then say the following phrase:

> *"I am opening up to allow my feelings of guilt to surface."*

Continue to process information as before. If you know you have other issues (such as jealousy or resentment) that you can't seem to bring to the surface, try to concentrate on those feelings.

I recommend that you practice these exercises 4 to 6 minutes per day for two weeks. They are especially helpful in getting you to stretch the diaphragm and relax.

After the third week, practicing 2 to 3 times per week is sufficient. (When you reach the chapter on pattern release (Chapter 11), you will need to practice daily.) Be certain to stretch the diaphragm as you do the exercises. Remain loose and limber so that you can feel your thoughts.

Exercise 3: Holding Your Breath to Relax

Holding your breath and inhaling are different aspects of breathing, and it is possible to hold your breath while taking in a short breath. In this exercise, take in a breath over 4 to 8 counts with the intention of holding it perhaps as much as 12 to 16 counts. Do not, under any circumstances, hold it longer than is comfortable. This is not a contest; it is health practice, and you are supposed to feel better, not worse. So start slowly and build up.

Wherever you are comfortable, inhale a medium breath, and then, as you are holding it, repeat to yourself one of these words every two or three counts:

STILL . . . STILL . . . STILL . . . STILL

PEACE . . . PEACE . . . PEACE . . . PEACE

QUIET . . . QUIET . . . QUIET . . . QUIET

CALM . . . CALM . . . CALM . . . CALM

You may use any word that you find comforting and relaxing, including "God," "Christ," "love," "joy," or "patience." You are giving yourself the message of quiet, peace, or calm by repeating the words in a relaxed state induced by holding the breath. It is very convincing to the mind. Even if you practice this exercise when you're not under pressure, the calming effects will be activated when you feel stressed.

Finally, finish breathing in one of two ways: If you are particularly tense, slowly exhale and sigh, *"AAhhh,"* for a few breaths. Generally, however, you will be so calm that exhaling through the nose will be sufficiently relaxing.

Breathing in this manner for 3 to 5 minutes should calm you under most circumstances, especially if you have been practicing in nonstressful situations. Part of the reason the technique works is that the mind is quieted by the breath and is more receptive to these messages than it would be if you repeated them in your usual breathing pattern. Your mind prefers calm to chaos, and if you practice enough, you will do the exercises even if you do not consciously recall them.

I recommend that you practice this exercise daily for 3 to 5 minutes. When you are under stress, breathe until you feel comfortable. Try different words and see which ones work best. Your mind is already preprogrammed for certain words, but you may have to experiment.

Exercise 4: Exhaling to Facilitate Emotional Release

When you exhale, you are not only exhaling air, you are giving your mind a message about release. Once you learn how to send your mind the message, it will be happy to facilitate the release of emotion.

In this exercise you are to inhale over 4 to 8 counts, hold for 4 to 6 counts, and then exhale while instructing your mind what to release. On the exhale, blow out with a "straw" for 4 to 8 counts. As you do so, say within:

> *"As I exhale, I can release the anger held deep down inside."*

> *"I am releasing the anger held deep down inside."*

> *"I freely and willingly release the anger deep down inside."*

As in the previous exercise, take time to process any feelings that may surface. If nothing seems to surface, that's okay. You are programming yourself for future release and saying the triggering words that will work when the time comes. With even a little practice, your mind will come to understand that you are willing to release emotion and that the breathing is an integral part of that process.

The four basic emotions that you want to work with now are anger, fear, sadness, and guilt. Repeat the same phrases as above but substitute the other three words. If you feel that there are other key words to indicate feelings you want to release, by all means use them.

I recommend that you practice this exercise once daily for a week. Spend only one or two minutes on each of the four emotions.

These simple breathing exercises should prepare you to move on to the next chapter, "Developing Awareness."

CHAPTER 6

DEVELOPING AWARENESS

To experience your emotional energy flows in a useful way, you must become more sensitive to the subtleties of their movement. You already feel the large flows— feelings such as fear, confusion, shame, and grief—and probably know precisely when they begin (with all the gentleness of a speeding freight train) and end. There are, however, feelings of a different order: the feelings generated when you walk, talk, and eat.

Bodily sensations occur when you wiggle your toes or hold back a sneeze. All of these little feelings contain keys to deeper, more powerful feelings, and these deeper feelings have more to do with the physical sensations associated with behaviors than they do with emotions. Nevertheless, bodily feelings are important because in this life we either think/feel or we behave. Sleeping, for example, doesn't seem to require much effort but is extremely important to our well-being. Our ability to tune into our "behaving" feelings will sensitize us to what constitutes a full spectrum of energies in motion: the *E-motions* of life.

Recall from Chapter 3 that the irregular, chaotic excess emotions are at the root of most people's problems. Many things can affect our moods in a very profound way.

The next sections contain details about sharpening your awareness. The exercises will help you to understand, utilize, and improve your skills.

BECOMING AWARE

Awareness is something that can be developed and improved, similar to reading skills. First, you learn little words written big, and then you get to big words written little. I will first ask you to become aware of your body through breathing and relaxation. Then I will show you how to become aware of your body through discovery of the creativity of your mind through imagery. (Imagery is a tool that can be employed in an infinite number of ways and will be covered in more detail in Chapter 7.) As awareness develops, you learn to feel your body respond as you repeat certain words or thoughts.

Start to become aware by focusing your attention. If I ask you to consider the size of the big toe on your right foot without looking at it, you must first find your right big toe as it exists in your mind, which is different from simply looking down at your feet. When you have found your right toe in your mind, then you can consider its size.

In order to consider something, you must be more than generally aware of it; you should have knowledge of its dimensions in inches, or its weight in ounces, for example. The process of paying specific attention is the way you gain awareness or knowledge. Thus, by thinking about a certain subject, such as your big toe, thoughts and feelings will arise as you concentrate on your toe. By thinking, you determine your mind's direction. The more precisely you know what to pay attention to, and the longer and more energetically you pay this attention, the deeper your awareness becomes.

Another way to think about this concept is as a conversation. It is the difference between listening attentively to someone and vaguely hearing the words but not really understanding them. When we absorb every word in a conversation, we gain a greater understanding of what the other person is trying to say. In this case, the other person happens to be ourself (deep down inside).

With this new attentiveness, breathing will be a new experience. By breathing in different ways and emphasizing different parts of the breathing cycle, you will learn many things about yourself, especially when you are relaxed or when you are tense. You will become aware of the way your mind can be used to generate images, and how these images can be used to relieve tension or help you reach various goals. As you focus more intently, you will become aware of the inner you and how your thoughts, feelings, mind, and body are connected. And with awareness of these feelings comes an understanding of what they mean.

Awareness is experienced in degrees. As you become more skilled, you develop a deeper level of awareness. There are no limits to awareness. The exercises in this chapter will help you reach the minimal levels of awareness that are necessary to achieve well-being.

It is even possible to become aware of something outside yourself. For example, an awareness of someone else's feelings, including physical pain, exists around us in a way that others can sense. It is often possible to feel what others are feeling. You may already be able to experience this level of awareness with loved ones.

For example, a person you know well says that he or she is feeling okay, but you don't believe it despite all reassurances. You can call it many things—intuition, vibes, or sensitivity—

but I prefer to call it *expanded awareness.* You may be receiving information through the person's voice, facial expressions, or a change in gait. You are especially attentive because, whether you are conscious of it or not, you have catalogued his or her previous behavior with great awareness and know or sense when there is a difference.

EXERCISES IN AWARENESS

Before you can reach this complex level of awareness of yourself, you need to start with some exercises to develop simple awareness. One way of finding out about yourself is by becoming aware of every action and movement you make. If you slow or stop certain actions, you'll discover that you've developed habits about why you do them. You probably take for granted actions such as sitting, walking, talking, eating, and maybe even driving. Take a moment now to become aware of your everyday activities.

Exercise 1: General Body Awareness

Sitting

Sit down for a couple of minutes and just be aware of sitting. First, notice how you are sitting. Are your legs crossed? Where are your feet and arms? How do you hold your back? After you've discovered yourself, change to a different position, one that you don't normally use. Stay in that position until you feel the urge to move, and then resist it. Where does the desire to move come from? Why are you uncomfortable? What feelings are generated? Pain? Tension? Anger?

Now get into a comfortable position and very slowly begin to rise from your chair. What muscle groups do you use? Rise up only halfway and hold that position for about 30 seconds. Notice what feelings surface as you struggle to do this exercise.

Walking

Notice how you walk. Look at your stride. Shorten it, lengthen it. Again, make yourself a little uncomfortable to gain awareness. Look at how you put your foot down; alter your rhythm. You must change your pattern to be aware of the one you normally adopt. Some of your choices of physical movement will depend on your height and weight, but many other teachings and variables enter into how you walk. Sit in a shopping mall or restaurant and watch people walk. Try to sense what they are like by how they move. Does the way they walk affect how you feel toward them? Can you dislike someone because he or she doesn't walk "right"?

Talking

Although you know how to talk, you may not be aware that what you're doing is mimicking what you've heard. If you had your voice box removed, you'd actually have to *learn* how to talk all over again. When alone, talk out loud and try to figure out how you know how to make the sounds. Notice the subtleties involved in making high- or low-pitched sounds. How did you produce those sounds? Play with taking in air in different amounts.

Eating

Next time you eat, notice how you chew. How well do you chew your food? How quickly do you take the next bite? Do you finish chewing and swallowing before you start on a new bite, or do you start on a new bite without chewing the last one? Are you in a hurry? Slow down and try to get the most out of each bite. How does that feel? Are you frustrated? What pleasure do you get from stuffing an already stuffed mouth?

Driving

For your sake as well as that of others, be aware of how you drive. How do you hold the wheel? Are you squeezing it tight? If so, relax. Where are your shoulders? Are you uptight? Sense your breathing. Is it rapid? Do you feel fearful? If so, where do you notice it?

Exercise 2: Awareness of Pain

Begin by identifying a pain anywhere in your body. Try to resist the impulse to take a pain reliever just long enough to gain awareness from the pain. Locate the boundaries of the pain so that its shape and dimension can be described. For example, is it in the middle of your stomach in a circle about two inches around? Now try to move that pain in all directions—up, down, left, right, front, and back. Did it move?

Next, try to find the rhythm of the pain. Pain is caused in large measure from nerve impulses periodically stimulating an area. If you focus, you will notice that the pain is not a constant feeling but a series of impulses with breaks in between. If it is not too intense, you should be able to notice it diminish. What happens when you follow the rhythm? Can you make it go faster or slower? Now go into the pain. Think of your pain as a hole, and project your mind into the hole as deep as you can go. What do you find there? Do you get any intuitions? Did any part of you "speak up"?

Finally, pretend your hand is a shovel and scoop up the pain as you would sand and remove it from its source. Move it from where it hurts, and throw it outside of your body. What happens as you do so? What are you aware of?

Exercise 3: Making Pain

It may seem odd to create pain, but I include this important exercise to make a point: *If you can make a pain, you can make it go away.*

In a place where you don't have a pain—perhaps your right index finger—tell yourself there is a pain at the tip of the finger. Can you feel it? Move the feelings down toward your wrist, stopping at each knuckle. Tell yourself how painful it is and that you are moving this pain down into your wrist so it will go away. When it reaches your wrist, be aware of how painful it is. Do you feel worried and concerned that it is not getting any better? Why?

Exercise 4: Emotion and Awareness

Think of something about which you are fearful—for example, flying in an airplane or fearing what will happen if you tell someone something that he or she doesn't want to hear. Imagine the situation in enough detail to stimulate your fear response. As feelings develop in your belly, for example, follow the feelings around so that you find out how deep your gut response is, just as you have done with pain. Does it begin in the front and go to the back? Does it go all the way to the spine? Where does it stop? Why did it stop there?

Burrow into the feeling as you did before, as if it were a hole, and try to find its depth. What do you notice? Come back out and follow all the manifestations of the fear. Follow any funny feelings in your legs or where your throat tightens up. Burrow into the throat feelings. Are they different from the belly feelings? Does focusing attentively and in great detail make the feelings better or worse? Why do you suppose that is?

Exercise 5: Exaggeration

While seated comfortably in a chair with your feet on the floor and arms at your sides, think of a disturbing memory that causes you some pain or anxiety. As you replay the memory, be aware of any subtle movements in your legs or arms, trunk or head. If something begins to move, exaggerate it, taking the movement to its full expression.

For example, if your pinky bends a little, follow it through so that it completely contracts. If you notice your legs beginning to close, as if to protect your genitals, follow it through. As you continue to experience the memory, see if you feel better when legs close protectively.

By exaggerating any movement to its maximum, you can see how reliving a thought moves your body. Exaggeration, as you will find, is very useful in bringing out feelings that are hidden and that need to be brought up and out. Practice exaggerating the movements in slow motion to better observe what your body does when stimulated in this way.

Work with these exercises until you can find and move the sensations in your body at will. It is very important that you know how much control you really have. As you will discover, when you become aware of hidden feelings, they change or disappear altogether. You will find that pain is much different from what you imagined and that it is not static but ever-changing.

Now that you have completed your bodily awareness exercises, it is time to work with the more traditional feelings of anger, love, and despair. Earlier, I compared the onrush of strong emotions with a speeding freight train. There are times when emotions are more subtle and come from deep down inside, where they are hidden and not understood. Many people

I see are amazed at how many hidden feelings they have. It is this "tip of the iceberg" effect that keeps you from dealing effectively with your problems. Many times, when you think you have forgotten about a feeling, something will happen to prove that it's still with you.

Next, we turn to the path of self-discovery and healing through the use of imagery and association.

CHAPTER 7

IMAGERY AND ASSOCIATION

It's not uncommon for people to think that the psychological process deals only with words. In reality, there is great value in the use of pictures and feelings. However, imagery is part of your daily life, whether or not you are aware of it.

It is currently believed that our brains are divided into two separate functional sides—the left brain, or logical, verbal side; and the right brain, or nonlinear, imaginative side. Although it's likely that people are predominantly either left-brain or right-brain types, all of us use both aspects of thinking.

One type of imaginative experience that seems to be universal is triggered by music. Everyone—young or old, rich or poor, educated or uneducated—enjoys some types of music and dislikes others. Imagery, in connection with music, is a universal phenomenon wherein one hears a song or piece of music and is transported to a past scene where it was first heard or first developed meaning. Songs can be associated with school, work, love, or a special event. If you hear a song and the memory image appears, then you are experiencing imagery. In fact, music is so powerful that it may not be possible to avoid the image or feeling. Often songs reminiscent of former lovers may be too painful to listen to.

Our mental images and musical sounds are so entwined that they cannot be separated. The process by which one part of an image brings to mind another part is called *association*. You remember better when you associate or put one image next to the other. If I were to ask, "What did you have for dinner at your sister-in-law's wedding ten years ago?" you might say, "I can't remember. It was too long ago." But if I were to remind you this was the night Uncle Joe spilled marinara sauce all over your white jacket, you would begin to get the picture.

Images include feelings too. Everything you have done in the past, you did because it felt right at the time. You constantly reference your experiences with your thoughts. That's part of memory, part of your internal images. In truth, you are constantly imaging. It is how you communicate within yourself. (I will talk more about inner communication in Chapter 12.)

THE THREE-PART IMAGE AND THE ENERGETIC FLOW

All images contain at least three parts: a *visual*, or seeing part; an *auditory*, or hearing part; and a *kinesthetic*, or feeling part. Occasionally you may also factor in taste or smell. Thus, if you have a feeling, there must be pictures and words with it; if you have a picture, there must be words or feelings; and if there are words, there must be pictures and feelings.

Experiments with age regression during hypnosis have shown that people have the ability to recall the moment of their birth with words and pictures that can be verified as being accurate. Unless you are blind or deaf, you have these associations built into you. The three-part image is the way you are built, and it is particularly valuable when feeling exists without recollection as to how or why it is there. This three-part system means that the reason for the feeling must exist somewhere within you, if only you look deeply enough.

Imagery, then, is a part of your everyday living and is not something unique or special. The only thing special about it is the way in which you explore and use your inner images to improve your well-being.

IMAGERY AND THE BIOFEEDBACK CONNECTION

Let's examine one more concept about imagery before you begin your exercises. At one time it was thought to be nearly impossible to control any of the internal organs or the autonomic or automatic nervous system. Occasionally, stories surfaced about some mysterious yogi who claimed to have control of these functions. He meditated for decades in a remote mountain cave, and his secret seemed unknowable. However, in the early 1960s the first biofeedback devices were developed. These devices gave feedback (information) regarding the status of a particular muscle or gland within a subject. The person could then, by trial and error, figure out how to alter the muscle or gland, usually by learning to relax or contract it.

One of the techniques developed to facilitate this process was the use of imagery. It was found that by imagining the way a muscle looked when it was relaxed, it would become relaxed. It was also possible to imagine a quiet, relaxing place and achieve a similar effect. It was as if the images, via the controlling brain, were communicating with the muscle in some way, either by directly telling it to relax or by convincing it that everything was fine and not to be tense. Technology was developed quickly that would affect every muscle, organ, blood vessel, and nerve in the body. Experiments demonstrated the ability to influence a single muscle fiber, heretofore an impossible feat.

You can reasonably expect to have an effect on a part of your body when you are imaging. *You do make a difference!* Your mind will do what it is told, unless there is some subconscious objection to it doing so.

BEGINNING EXERCISES IN IMAGERY

Find a comfortable chair and sit with your back straight, both feet on the floor, and your arms at your sides. Wear comfortable clothing that isn't tight or constricting, and be sure there are no distractions. Take a couple of deep breaths. Let's first practice with an image of general body awareness.

General Body Awareness Exercise

One of the most important images that you can have is your ability to increase your general body awareness (see Chapter 6). Much of the change process comes from being aware of your present status. I would like you to be able to sit down at any time or place and be aware of how you feel in different parts of your body. In this first exercise, I'll give you some general ideas that you can adapt to suit your own needs. Remember, there is no one right way to do this—whatever helps you to be more well is what is correct.

Find a comfortable place to sit in the neutral position. (That is, arms at your sides and legs together. See Figure 10A in Chapter 5.) Close your eyes and begin the process with easy deep breathing. I recommend that you inhale for six counts, hold your breath for six counts, and exhale for six counts. Repeating this four to five times should be sufficient.

Beginning at the top of your head, *intend* to be aware of how you feel. Scan yourself internally, up and back, right and left, as if a light or some scanning device were checking every portion of you. Make sure that nothing is missed. You must spend some moments in each place in order to get all the information. Initially, this process may take some time.

Now, from the top of your head in an orderly fashion, *be aware* of how your scalp feels. Is it tight, or hot, or numb? Be aware of your scalp moving forward and backward, left and right. If there is an area of tension or other feeling, just experience it—don't try to fix it or make it go away.

Move your awareness next into your entire head, mentally going inside as if you could feel your brain. Continue into your forehead, moving left and right and then down your face, methodically going over and around your eyes, nose, lips, mouth, cheeks, chin, and jaw. Be aware of the difference in feeling between the right and left, following any feelings inside, trying to find their origin. Continue to move into your neck, front and back, left and right. Most certainly the front and back will be different. In what ways is this so? Make an effort to find words for your feelings. You will notice that focusing your attention for a few seconds will bring to the surface sensations that had previously escaped you.

Move next to your shoulders, front and back, left and right. Then focus your attention on each arm, moving slowly down the arm, from shoulder to biceps to elbow, forearm, wrist, palm, and then each individual finger. If there is an area of pain or discomfort, go inside it mentally, and imagine that you're looking for the origin of the pain. As you did in the previous chapter ("Developing Awareness"), find the precise boundaries of any pain, so that you can identify a distinct pain or discomfort.

After you have attended to your arms, go down your back, from your neck to your hips, *slowly* making certain that you know the differences between left and right. After you have done your back, move to your front. Pay special attention to your breathing. Find where there is any resistance to a natural inhalation. Put your attention into that and see what happens. Tune into your heart. Can you sense it beating? Very slowly cross the diaphragm and move down into the abdominal cavity. Remember not to rush, and give yourself a chance to be aware of the feelings that are there. If you go too quickly, you'll miss them. In the following exercises, it is essential that you be aware of the subtleties of feelings that exist within you.

Move down into your pelvis, right and left, front and back. Make an effort to sense your sex organs. When you do so, do you get pictures or thoughts? From there follow each leg one at a time—thigh, knee, shin, calf, ankle, foot, and into each toe. Are your legs identical?

After you've completed the whole body, stay in the neutral position for a minute or two. It is a good place from which to start other exercises.

In the sections ahead, when I ask you to feel your thoughts, it will be important for you to be able to describe your present state of feeling in a more in-depth way than merely saying, "I feel happy . . . sad . . . a little tense," or "I have a headache." When you have completed this exercise for the first time, make an effort to return to it a few hours later. It will go much faster the next time, and you'll also notice how much change has taken place since the first time. Note how much more you feel as opposed to what you *thought* you felt when you first sat down. Most people have no idea how they really feel in their bodies until they spend several minutes of very direct attention.

Ideally, you should try to take a few minutes daily to find out how you feel. Certainly, prior to doing any in-depth work, it is essential. If you feel ill or agitated, it is important to go inside for a deeper scan. With practice, this will take only a few minutes. In fact, it takes longer to read about or describe the technique than to do it.

REAL-LIFE IMAGES

I now turn your attention to a different kind of image—one that represents real life. These images are vignettes drawn from hypothetical but real experiences.

Before doing these imaging exercises, return to the General Body Awareness Exercise and spend a few minutes scanning your body.

Image #1

Imagine that you have just finished preparing dinner and are sitting home alone, awaiting the arrival of your spouse or significant other. You are very hungry and are expecting that person to come through the door any minute. The silence is broken by a telephone call from the Highway Patrol. They inform you that there has been a serious accident on the freeway and that you'd better come to the hospital right away. You put the phone down. How do you feel? Are you calm or anxious? Take a moment to think about your body's reactions.

If you can even vaguely identify with this scene, you may find yourself quite upset. Your feelings are coming from what you imagined has happened. Actually, all that has happened is that I provided the words, you made a picture, and from that picture or pictures your body responded with what you call feelings. If you felt something, your body changed, and different chemicals were produced. The feelings you're generating may have cumulative effects over time.

Image #2A

Imagine that you've been having a lot of gas and heartburn lately. Your spouse has invited critical, demanding, complaining Aunt Tillie to stay with you for a two-month visit. Even though you can barely stand to eat Christmas dinner with her, you go along with the plan. It is now time for her arrival, and you are sitting in your living room, waiting for the car to pull up. You hear the car and go outside and remove her luggage from the trunk of the car. Notice how the luggage feels as you carry it upstairs to the guest room. Does it seem heavy? How do you feel? How about that stomach condition?

Image #2B

You are awaiting the arrival of that special someone whom you haven't seen for a long time and whom you have missed very much. You are in the living room when you hear the car pull up. You go outside to get the luggage out of the trunk and take it up to the guest room. How does your stomach feel? How heavy is the luggage?

Are you having trouble imagining these different feelings? Would it help if I were to describe an autopsy of a person who had been shot and found in the bushes two weeks later? Shall I describe the condition of his flesh? No? Why not? Would you find the description of rotting, putrid flesh disgusting? If so, you are just imagining it, for there is nothing here but the black ink, the white paper, and your mind.

Now that you are aware that you can *feel* and *see* and *hear* images, consider what effect your own description of your life might have on your body. Let's try another example on this topic of feeling imagery.

Image #3

Suppose that you're about 50 years old. You've been working steadily for the same company for the last 15 years in a job that pays the bills and affords a few creature comforts but gives you no personal satisfaction. You've been saving every penny to start your own business—a lifelong dream. You believed that you and your spouse agreed that you would quit your present job and start the new business as soon as you had enough money.

Lately, though, your spouse has been opposed to the idea and is doubting the wisdom of such a plan and your ability to make a go of the business. He or she is afraid of falling behind financially and is concerned about how you would feel if you were to fail. Basically, he/she is very fearful and negative about the whole thing. You can't imagine remaining with the company for the rest of your life, or even for the five years it would take before you can retire early. You try to figure out a solution to this unexpected conflict.

Take a few moments to assess your thoughts and feelings. What will you do? Will you do what you desire and live your dream, or will you maintain peace in the household at any cost? Go from your head to your toes and assess your feelings throughout your body in this hypothetical situation. Can you imagine how it feels to be stuck, unable to live and do things the way you'd always hoped, to be trapped by the very person you love and who loves you? What effect do you suppose a long-term frustration can have on you and your body?

Image #4

You're a woman in your forties who has never worked and whose youngest child is leaving home tonight. You're proud of having been a good mother. In fact, it's been the most important focus of your life, so much so that you don't know how to do anything else. Your husband works too much, and, if the truth be known, your relationship with him hasn't really been close for years.

Now imagine yourself at home alone looking out the window. How do you feel? Take a moment to sense if your eyes feel teary, or your throat tightens. Is your chest heavy or light? How is your breathing? And your shoulders—are they down or up? Do you feel a kind of sticking or tingling sensation in your chest or abdomen?

If you've successfully imagined any of the foregoing scenes, it should be clear that what you think and feel makes a difference to your body and that you can notice changes through imagery. When you experience life, whether in reality or in your fantasies, you feel it deep down inside. What you know and live with are the accumulated daily remembrances of imagery and the feelings generated, both good and bad, that stimulate your body. Because you are busy living life, you fail to sense the day-to-day accumulation of ideas, feelings, and behaviors that come into your life.

The accumulation of energies is more powerful than you realize. Your emotional pain or joy is additive. Frustration experienced on a daily basis is worse than frustration experienced weekly, monthly, yearly, or "once in a blue moon." I emphasize this because your emotional and psychological responses to everyday situations have been grossly underestimated in terms of their effect on your total health. All your feelings of depression, anger, fear, confusion, and loneliness are recorded in your physical body. If you are ever to be truly well, you must recognize this and use the psychoenergetics exercises described in this book to achieve your goals.

We now turn to more healing image pictures that can diminish or eliminate unpleasant feelings.

Therapeutic Imagery Exercises

Here we will use imagery in a directed, therapeutic way. Many of you who have cancer or AIDS may find these exercises helpful. (Also see Chapter 14, "Cancer Imagery.")

Color

The simplest type of image involves imagining different colors. If you can see yourself in a red dress or a charcoal suit, you can generate images in living color. The most effective way to use color imagery is to imagine different colors as they flow through the body. The idea is to run the colors through your body with some specific intention. Different colors seem to have different effects. Try using these colors to achieve the following benefits.

WHITE	Cleansing or clearing the body
BLUE	Calming and cooling for pain
GREEN	Calming and healing
YELLOW	Increasing mental clarity
PINK	Increasing "loving" feelings
RED	Generally activating and stimulating or warming
PURPLE	Enhancing or stimulating a spiritual sense within
GOLD	Gently activating, as well as enhancing your ability to feel spiritual and "loving"

These basic colors may be imagined as flowing through the body from the top of the head to the feet and into the ground, or from the ground up through the body to the head. The image of color flowing from your head to your toes is used to enhance or activate in a subdued manner. As the color goes through to the feet, it is said to be "grounding" or stabilizing. The reverse—from the ground up—has a more exciting quality as it moves toward the head.

You can send color (also thought of as light) from the right shoulder to the right thumb without going through the whole body, likewise from the left hip to the left knee. The color or light is best started a bit away from the part being enhanced. It tends to give it a running start. It is, however, possible to imagine only one spot, such as the right shoulder.

Now that you know what the colors can stimulate, try these exercises:

1. Imagine a white light beginning at the top of your head. See it flow through your scalp, forehead, eyes, nose, mouth, jaw, and neck as it cleanses and clears away sadness (poisons, anxiety, dead cancer cells) from the body. Allow it to continue through your shoulders, down your arms, through your hands, into the palms, and then through the fingers. The white light also moves through your chest, including your heart, lungs, and diaphragm. It continues down the back, cleansing and clearing the shoulder blades and spinal cord, all the way down to the level of the hips. It can also be seen to cleanse and clear the abdominal area, including the gall bladder, liver, pancreas, spleen, and intestines, as it makes its way through the pelvis and all of the pelvic organs down into the hips, legs, knees, shins, ankles, feet, and down into the ground. It's actually easier to see it

than to say or write it. Obviously, you can substitute any color or type of enhancement.

2. Send a green light into a surgical scar—be it on the chest, abdomen, or right earlobe. See it healed, whole, and healthy. See these images for two to three minutes at least four, six, or even eight times per day. Healing images seem to work best, in my experience, when done for short periods on a frequent basis rather than trying to hold an image for twenty minutes once or twice a day.

   You can see the colors and do the exercises anywhere you can get comfortable, whether at home, the office, or somewhere else.

IMAGES OF LETTING GO

Sometimes it's very important to be able to let go of something, whether it be a loved one, an idea, or a pain. For example, suppose you are separated or divorced and can't let go. Imagine your hand letting go of your former spouse's hand. Or picture a helium balloon filled with your feelings. Let it go; watch it float into the sky; and feel the release as it floats higher and higher.

Perhaps you wish life to flow on but are having difficulty letting it do so. Picture a river flowing past you, or see an object belonging to a person that you wish to let go of floating on the river. There is nothing that can be done to release the pain until you are willing to let go of the idea. Other aspects of letting go involve body positioning, which will be taken up at a later time (see "Visualization and Pattern Release" Chapter 13).

Here are some additional examples of letting-go images. Your success in letting go can be measured by how well your image conforms to your intention.

ANGER	You come home as your house is being robbed. Your Doberman has just bitten the burglar's hand. You command the dog to release the hand and watch as its teeth release him.
CONTROL	A bird in your hand, symbolizing what needs to go, flies away as you release your grasp. Imagine letting go of the steering wheel of your car and allowing it to go where it will.
DEPRESSION	Lift a rock off your back or chest. Put your worries into a balloon and let them go.
GUILT	Let yourself or someone else out of jail, and see the door close and lock behind you.

Next, let's take a close look at how emotions affect our lives.

CHAPTER 8

YOUR EMOTIONS

Before delving into your mind to uncover the awareness deep down inside, first you need to understand one core concept: the true nature of emotion. In this chapter you will begin to study your emotions in greater depth. You will learn about the importance of emotions in your life, the properties of emotions, and some of the myths that surround them.

WHY STUDY EMOTIONS AT ALL?

The principal reason to study emotions in a methodical way is that emotions are frequently accompanied by unnecessary pain. Few people are able to find the middle ground in accepting and expressing this part of themselves. Most either attempt to repress and eliminate all emotions entirely or become helplessly caught up in their emotions. Many feel trapped, as if caught in a fierce storm that takes them wherever the wind blows, leaving them feeling vulnerable and uneasy, and often in great pain. There is, however, a better way to manage our emotions. First, we must understand them and how they function within us.

What Is Emotion?

Emotion is defined in *Taber's Medical Dictionary* as "a mental state or strong feeling affect usually accompanied by physical changes in the body, such as alteration in heart rate and respiratory activity, vasomotor reactions, and changes in muscle tone." Emotion is further described as "a mental state or feeling such as fear, hate, love, anger, grief, and joy." These feelings constitute the drive that brings about the emotional or mental adjustment necessary to satisfy instinctive needs.

By definition, then, emotions have a definite physical or biological component that is measurable in one or more organs. Without these changes and the chemicals that cause them, no one really experiences an emotion. Taber's also defines an emotion as a feeling, an instinctive drive, which is an integral part of what life is about. *"Physiological changes invariably accompany alteration in the emotions,"* Taber's goes on, *"but such change may not be apparent to either the person experiencing emotion or an observer."*

Initially, the small, subtle changes that occur during an emotional experience may not be felt at all; but they are there. It is this failure to notice changes associated with emotion that will be addressed in the exercises to come. Much of the work in the psychofeedback exercises in Chapter 9 is based on the knowledge that emotional and physiological changes exist and have specific meaning for you in terms of what you think and feel *deep down inside.* As your body loosens and you become more comfortable with sensing your feelings, these previously unfelt emotions will become obvious and undeniable. The unexperienced become experienced, and you come to know yourself in a different way.

Also of importance is the definition of the word "feeling." *Webster's* defines feeling as "the power or faculty of experiencing physical sense; an awareness; consciousness; sensation as a feeling of pain; an emotion." Here feeling and emotion are defined synonymously, as an experience of physical sensation—a sensation in the body somewhere—not a thought. As you will see, this is the crux of the definition. When you make a statement like, "Yesterday, I felt silly," you must be able to identify precisely the physical sensation of silliness and state exactly where in (or on) the body it was located.

If you can't precisely define what and where you experience a feeling, such as embarrassment, shame, foolishness, childishness, stupidity, or luck, you are out of touch with your feelings. Being out of touch with your feelings means that you don't know what physiological processes are going on inside of you. And not knowing what's going on inside you may be dangerous to your health.

For example, you may have heard of someone who went to the doctor "feeling fine," only to be told that he or she was very sick. People like that may be out of touch with their feelings and unaware of the little changes that gradually became big changes. Are you beginning to see the importance of being in touch with your feelings?

PROPERTIES OF EMOTIONS AND FEELINGS

Now let's look at some of the properties, or qualities, that make up emotions/feelings in order to understand why they affect us as they do. Emotions are an electrochemical phenomenon consisting of two parts. The electrical component allows emotions to move rapidly through you, via the nervous system, often reaching the target area faster than you can utter a response. This seemingly instantaneous movement tells you that the ultimate control is subconscious, or unconscious, since it occurs faster than you can think; thus, it is to the unconscious that you must look in order to gain ultimate mastery or balance of your emotions. At this point, this unconscious mind has been unknown to you for the most part. But as you study and complete the exercises in this book, you will see that your unconscious mind pretty well matches your conscious mind, though it can also be quite contrary and rebellious. This "difference of opinion" within yourself is the source of your emotional conflicts.

The second, and perhaps more important, quality of emotion is its chemical nature. This property allows emotion to be collected or stored indefinitely, as opposed to disappearing soon after it is experienced. The chemical nature of emotion is proven by the phenomenon of memory.

Think of any highly emotional event, either positive or negative (a marriage, death, or divorce), and concentrate on it for awhile. See it, hear it, and soon you will feel it. You may not experience the same intensity of feeling as you did originally, but even recalled emotions can be intense, depending on how much feeling or affect has been released already. The feeling is precisely recorded in the place in your body that you first experienced it.

It is also possible for additional associations to be formed from an old image, which could add feelings to the memory. Frequently, one memory leads to others, which may be even more significant than the first. Each has its own storehouse of emotional energy. Your memory bank faithfully stores the pictures and sounds that can stimulate the same feelings in the same place, over and over again, just as they were experienced originally.

It is very important to be able to remove or discharge feelings from your memory so that when you recall them, it appears more like a one-dimensional photograph rather than an emotional experience.

Emotional pain is more deeply and accurately recorded than pure physical pain. For example, if you made a big fuss about how much it would hurt when the dentist told you your wisdom teeth had to be pulled, the dental pain may be poorly recalled, but the emotional pain, your embarrassment about the big fuss, can be recalled and reexperienced quite easily.

As a therapist, I can state unequivocally that everyone fears emotional pain far more than physical discomfort. I routinely ask, "Which would you rather have, a broken heart or a broken leg?" A broken leg wins every time. Not only negative feelings are remembered, of course. Pride, joy, or a romantic evening can also be pulled from your memory bank with equal ease.

You might be wondering how it is known that emotion is not stored in your brain and only appears later in your body. One way of knowing is to notice, as you do the exercises that will release emotions from your body, that you feel relief in the body part first and only later experience mental relief as you think about the feelings and add words to them.

Discharging of Negative Emotion

The discharge of negative emotions is a very important part of your work and part of the reason you must learn to know your true feelings. By releasing the harmful effects of guilt, fear, anger, and depression, you will begin to feel and be better in many ways.

For example, if you call up a painful scene, perhaps viewing the casket of your dead mother, father, or spouse, you will experience some deep feelings, maybe a pain in your heart, or an ache or funny feeling in the pit of your stomach. Maybe tears will well up in your eyes. If I ask you to tell me about the same scene a week later, two months later, or even twenty years later, you might still have those feelings in the same places, though probably with less intensity. They will always be there in pretty much the same way because the picture, sound, and feeling have been recorded.

The Body Always Remembers

Additional evidence that your feelings are stored in your body and not in your brain is demonstrated by the techniques used in certain forms of bodywork. As a part of the body is stroked or massaged, powerful emotional memories suddenly emerge, although the mind was blank or on a totally unrelated thought just moments before. Ultimately, the phenomenon of "body memory" has to be experienced to be truly believed. I assure you that body memory is very real. We will now explore another very real phenomenon—the danger of holding emotion.

HOLDING EMOTION

An emotion has the following characteristics:

- *An emotion can be held inside indefinitely.*
- *An emotion can be added onto—that is, there is a "cumulative effect."*
- *An emotion can be overloaded, leading to explosion or implosion.*
- *An emotion is minimally dissipated by time.*

Perhaps most important:

- *An emotion can be discharged with intention and effort.*

These characteristics imply that stored emotions act like a chemical reservoir, which must be managed as if the chemicals were toxic. There are serious consequences to leaving stored negative energy unattended for any great length of time. Negative energy can be defined as energy derived from a negative emotional experience, such as hatred, anger, guilt, fear, or depression. Because emotional chemical energy can be stored, the subtle physiological changes associated with memory still exist. If left unchecked, these changes may continuously do harm.

In effect, stored negative emotion is a form of chronic stress. This form of stress is unrelated to dramatic or specific life events. This low-level stress wears on you day after day—unseen, unnoticed, unfelt—until one day the little changes add up to one huge change, which is called disease. A serious disease might even appear in someone who has never been sick at all. Negative emotional chemical energy has the potential to do harm by remaining in place and persistently causing stress on the body in the same area that first experienced the feeling.

For example, if not discharged, an angry feeling in the stomach continues to eat away at the stomach slowly, perhaps for many years, until it produces an ulcer, unless something is done to prevent it. These are verifiable medical facts that cannot be denied.

What isn't widely understood, however, is that the same sensation experienced in the bowels, the pancreas, or the thymus could also continue unconsciously. In fact, any place in the body where feeling is gathered or strongly felt might be affected years, even decades, later if no resolution is sought.

Once you know and accept that emotions remain intimately tied to your memories and beliefs and don't disappear when the event is over, you will want to release as much as you can, as quickly as you can.

Let's review some of the common myths about emotion in the next section. Try to dispel some of the myths that you once believed so that you can understand and utilize all of your emotional experiences, both good and bad, for enhancing your health.

MYTHS ABOUT EMOTIONS

In many respects, misunderstandings about emotions are societal in nature. Your inability to wisely handle your emotions doesn't necessarily evolve from bad parenting or poverty. Your inability to handle emotions comes from the intrinsic fear that your emotions make you too vulnerable and must be put aside or conquered. As a result, your mind defends you by denying, devaluing, and constricting this "tiger by the tail" as much as possible. The result is a series of beliefs that have no basis in fact and only serve to limit and diminish you and the quality of life you experience.

Myth 1: *Emotional expression does harm to others.*

It is commonly believed that an honest expression of emotion—including anger toward a friend or loved one—is harmful to that person or relationship. When questioned, cancer patients, regardless of their background, state that they believe this to be true. This belief may be a reaction to a home filled with anger and argument, or it may be a continuation of a home where no one was allowed to be angry or raise a voice. This is harmful in many ways.

First, lack of expression denies everyone around you an honest relationship. No one will ever know how you really feel, and an entire lifetime may be spent with no one saying what he or she really felt or what was on his or her mind. In addition, it assumes that people are more fragile than they really are, that a cross word or serious confrontation will cause them to collapse or "break down." In reality, most are quite well-equipped to handle a verbal confrontation, which is certainly far preferable to violence.

Again and again, I hear the concern, "So-and-so couldn't take it if I told the truth." Nonsense! Ironically, while you're protecting another from hurt, you're complaining about the lack of intimacy in your life. Intimacy implies honesty and is a deep, mutual sharing of both positive and negative feelings. Intimacy is more than time together or shared experience; it is self-disclosure that must include the whole truth, not a whitewashed version designed to minimize confrontation or anxiety.

This harmful "anti-intimacy" belief needs to be released—discarded from your mental warehouse—and there's no time like the present. Below is an affirmation to release this old belief. It is similar to the affirmation used in Alcoholics Anonymous, in which participants firmly state that they are powerless before alcohol.

You, too, are powerless before your beliefs unless you affirm your desire to be rid of them. Wishing will not make it happen; it requires determination, along with a strong, definitive statement of intention and desire. This is how you begin:

> ***"Without fear, doubt, or hesitation, I freely and willingly release all fears and false beliefs regarding the idea that honest emotional expression does harm to others."***

Repeat the phrase several times while seated quietly. Try to sense what you feel as you make the statements. From now on check yourself every day and notice how it feels.

Myth 2: *Emotions, once expressed, become uncontrollable.*

Another popular belief is that if you are honest—especially about anger or guilt—you might do something you would later regret. I suppose it's theoretically possible for this to happen. For example, if you were at the breaking point from suppressing your feelings over many years, and someone irritated or confronted you, you fear you might suddenly explode and want to hurt them. This is highly unlikely, but there is some truth in it. If you suppress enough anger or hatred, sooner or later you must either explode outwardly and do harm to others or implode and make yourself ill. If you constantly vent your feelings a little at a time in appropriate ways, they will never build up or get out of control.

Unfortunately, some people hold in their feelings for years and years, and when their emotional tank can't compress or suppress the emotion any more, POOF—they explode! The newspaper headlines are familiar, "Quiet Family Man Kills Wife and Five Children," or "Madman Kills 20 in Shopping Mall Murder Spree." Everyone wonders how such events could happen. So, if you wish to prevent outbursts, explosions, and other surprises, don't stuff your feelings or encourage the same in others. Express yourself. It's more natural and healthy. Decide now to release this myth by reading the affirmation below out loud.

"Without fear, doubt, or hesitation, I freely and willingly release all fears and false beliefs connected with the idea that emotional expression, once released, becomes uncontrollable."

Again, relax. Repeat the phrase out loud five more times, and with a little peace of mind go on to the next section.

Myth 3: *Emotions are more trouble than they're worth, and we're better off without them.*

This myth questions the value of emotions at all. But what would life be like without them? What would you be like without them? Could you live without desire, frustration, pride, or sorrow? Would you even be truly human? Do you not, in fact, experience life through your emotions? Is your life so filled with pain that you want only a bland, preprogrammed existence, devoid of challenges, defeats, sorrows, or losses? It's unrealistic to hope that perhaps there will come a time when only positive emotions exist. But you can learn to recognize and understand your emotions so that you can master and benefit by them.

Without feelings, there would be no motivation to do anything. We are motivated to do things because we feel better when we do them. We find love, work for success, or have children because it feels like the right thing to do. The belief that emotions are more trouble than they're worth, or the implication that only reason and thought have value, is an example of fearing unknown feelings. Interestingly, this belief is often held by those who are tired of experiencing long-term pain and who have become turned off to life. This reaction can occur at any age.

I recall a young woman with breast cancer who told me that she had decided one day when she was about 12 years old that she would never show anger, never trust, and never love too much because she had been badly hurt. Her decision had resulted in migraine headaches, ulcers, arthritis, and most recently, cancer. She knew that emotional repression had played a role in all of her illnesses, but she refused to deal with her feelings, believing that it was too late to change. After a few visits she never returned. Perhaps for some, a feeling existence is too painful to tolerate, but I hope that number is very small. To experience life and health, you must begin to affirm. Read this affirmation out loud:

> ***"Without fear, doubt, or hesitation, I freely and willingly release all fears and false beliefs about allowing myself to feel***

> ***all of my human feelings, both good and bad, and accept myself just as I am."***

Practice this affirmation five more times, and promise never to let yourself become a robot, unfeeling and unaware of life around you.

Myth 4: *Emotions are a sign of weakness.*

Here is another myth about emotions held by those who overvalue the mind to the detriment of their feeling natures. It seems that the tradition of stoicism, which began in ancient Greece, has persisted through the ages, as evidenced by the existence of many who believe that emotion is a weakness to be fought, like an addiction to liquor or gambling. These individuals overtly possess a superior attitude toward their peers and are rigid in their judgment of others. As you read the following descriptions, think about people you know who may think like this. The beliefs of the stoic can be summarized as follows:

1. **ANGER:** Indicative of lack of personal control, certainly never outwardly shown, and to be fought off at all costs.

2. **FEAR:** Never to be acknowledged, for it denotes cowardice, and you will lose respect from others and yourself if it is shown.

3. **DEPRESSION:** Equivalent to mental weakness. Women and weaklings get depressed. To ask for help is a disgrace. If you can't solve your own problems, there is something seriously wrong with you.

4. **GUILT:** Means you did something wrong, and it is never to be acknowledged in any way.

5. **LOVE:** Is theoretically a good idea, as long as one never feels too much, thus becoming vulnerable to irrational acts, as well as pain and sorrow.

Now, think about the people you know who exhibit these characteristics, ask yourself these questions: "How happy are they? How well do their lives work? How many friends do they have? How enjoyable are they to be around?"

According to the stoic, the only truly valuable experiences in life are based on discipline and rational thought. Emotional people are seen as wasting their time on foolish fluff. These emotions interfere with the real meaning of life, generally accepted as honor, success, power, and prestige. This kind of thinking involves beliefs that limit the richness of life and are inconsistent with optimum health. Stoics interfere with other people's experiences of life by belittling them for emoting and enjoying what they themselves cannot.

These beliefs represent a combination of many unhealthy patterns, which you will most certainly want to eliminate. Begin this emotional life-affirming process by saying out loud:

> ***"Without fear, doubt, or hesitation, I freely and willingly release all fears and false beliefs about the idea that enjoying and experiencing emotions is a sign of weakness that interferes with and diminishes my life."***

If this description fits you, you may need to repeat this affirmation 100 times or more before it begins to sink in. But whatever your belief, make a conscious effort to be open to all feeling states, both positive and negative.

Myth 5: *Emotional expression is useless after the fact.*

"Let bygones be bygones." In this myth, the person admits that an emotional expression may have had some value at one point, but after the event is over, it's a waste of time to dwell on it. These people acknowledge that they were angry, their stomach hurt, they felt lousy—but it's over now, so why rehash it all? The reason, of course, is that it's never really over until the emotion is released fully and completely. Remember, balance requires that "anger in" must be followed by "anger out" because emotions don't go away; they remain stored until they are discharged.

This principle can be best exemplified by the case of an attractive woman in her mid-forties who sought me out for treatment of chronic pain. She had multiple surgeries and was told that her pain was the result of adhesions (sticking together of tissues due to scarring). Before consulting me, this well-to-do lady had met with the finest specialists throughout the world who had told her there was nothing they could do. The woman was desperate and threatened to kill herself if she could not obtain relief from her pain.

We began to work with the pain and discovered much unresolved anger from her early childhood. She was highly motivated, and her desperation worked to her advantage. After several weeks of therapy, she found some very deep, old, emotional scars from which she was able to release a great deal of emotional pain. Not long afterward, she began to feel the physical pain diminish. When I followed up with her years later, she continued to remain well.

There is nothing unusual about this story. Time and time again, I have seen the value of looking at old, unresolved emotional issues and freeing the destructive energies held within.

The resulting relief of physical symptoms has at times been nothing short of amazing. As far as your body is concerned, there is no such thing as yesterday's news when the issue is still held deep down inside.

If you are ready to discard another myth, and wish to free as much negative energy as possible from your body, begin by affirming and saying out loud:

> ***"Without fear, doubt, or hesitation, I freely and willingly release all fears and false beliefs that somehow my emotions will just disappear and that there is no need to experience them after the fact."***

Say this phrase as many times as you need to. Tell yourself that you are willing to do whatever is necessary to find and release negative emotions.

Myth 6: *Emotions have no value other than the feeling state that they produce.*

Another belief is that emotions are simply psychobiologic experiences that simply happen and that have no further meaning. If anger is honestly expressed, or if depression is felt, and guilt acknowledged, what else can there be? What is there beyond balance?

Certainly, compared with suffering and suppressing your emotions, free expression is a great improvement, but there is yet another level of clarity to be achieved. This level requires that once you have acknowledged and expressed your emotions, you must begin to look at them and study them, to distance yourself from your experience and ask, "Why am I feeling this emotion? Where is it coming from? What underlies it?" Once you have honestly expressed your emotions and are feeling clear and healthy, you can begin to look at it.

Let's say you get angry. Isn't anger really about expectations and disappointments? How fair or realistic are those expectations? At some level your expectations are your own projections from inside made visible. Who is it that needs to change, and why can't you get people to do what you want? At this new, higher level of clarity, each angry event is a lesson unto itself.

Your new self will seek new challenges for growth. One way to do this is by studying those reflections called anger, fear, guilt, and depression. The real myth is that emotions and actions are somehow disconnected from the greater self. By working with these honest emotional expressions and reviewing them as part of your as-yet-unknown deeper self, you can discover why you feel and act as you do. Powerful emotional expressions are your teachers, as are your friends, your job, your illnesses, and whatever else is projected onto the screen of everyday life.

If you are ready to use your emotions to probe into the deepest part of yourself, affirm this by saying out loud:

"Without fear, doubt, or hesitation, I release all fears and false beliefs about seeing the reflections of emotions and using them for growth."

You now have the basics to begin your process of self-discovery and to use the information that you find. Perhaps the most important exercises you will do are found in the next chapter, "Psychofeedback."

CHAPTER 9

PSYCHOFEEDBACK

Awareness means knowing what you really think and feel *deep down inside.* The exercises in this chapter require that you consider your feelings about important life issues. I call these exercises *psychofeedback* because they give you feedback or information about yourself without the use of a machine (as in many biofeedback exercises). They require only that you pay attention to what you see in your mind's eye and what you feel in your body. The whole concept of healing through emotional release is premised on your knowing what you really think and feel *deep down inside,* as opposed to what you now believe you think and feel.

Most people don't know their true feelings until they're asked to defend their beliefs or precisely describe their philosophy of life. Even your personal philosophy about such things as honesty, morality, marriage, and child-rearing is based on an idealized version of how you would like to live, rather than how you really live.

Once you begin to explore your emotions using psychofeedback techniques, you'll discover that you frequently have two opinions on any subject: your conscious ideas, which you openly discuss or admit; and your unconscious or subconscious opinions. It is the latter that you use to make important life decisions. It is these subconscious opinions, those found *deep down inside,* that you are searching for now.

It's important that you be prepared for "differences of opinion" within yourself, or they'll trouble you and you won't be able to gain from the exercises. Remember that most people are unaware of their deepest beliefs. It is, I suppose, part of the essence of being human not to know ourselves. Our unhappiness and illness are an outgrowth of a lack of inner knowledge. (On a larger scale, I believe this is the cause for much of the unhappiness in the world.)

Up to this point, if you have done the exercises in previous chapters, you are somewhat prepared to expect the "unexpected," the duality of your conscious and unconscious thoughts. You can now learn psychofeedback techniques in order to discover yourself a little more deeply. After you have completed the Psychofeedback Self-Help Inventory, some of the applications will be obvious; others can be discussed. I'm sure that you will find new uses for this flexible and simple system.

INTRODUCTION TO SELF-DISCOVERY

It's important to take inventory of what you think about many life issues because everything that is in your life—your job, family, and friends—is a function of how you feel. The decisions you made in the past may no longer feel right for you now, but you aren't certain as to how to proceed.

The basic techniques of psychofeedback are simple but powerful. It is a methodical, logical, and self-validating approach. Self-validating means that you, not someone else, will acknowledge whether or not the information is valid.

There are three separate, but related, skills to learn: *visual feedback, feeling your thoughts and feeling your breath.* Each will be described in this chapter, accompanied by exercises.

Besides learning what you feel at this deeper level and accepting it as valid, there is another important concept to be learned. Thc newly discovered feelings are part of a large network of patterns like the words you actually use.

As you become more comfortable with communicating with yourself and feeling your feelings, the visual feedback and breathing will no longer become individual exercises, but an integrated system of self-awareness to help you become more aware of the changing moods and feelings that lie within you.

Stating False Belief Patterns

By being able to state the false belief patterns in one sentence, you have a tool to solve the underlying problems. For, as you recall, they are not just words but emotional energies contained in your "matrix" that can be released through the techniques in this book.

For example, suppose you feel that you have low self-esteem. The concept of self-esteem is vague and varies greatly from one person to another. The psychofeedback method asks that you inquire deep within yourself precisely how you feel. So, you must ask yourself specific questions such as "Am I not as good as other people?" "Is it that I am not pretty enough, smart enough, wealthy enough, or thin enough?" What does it mean not to like or love yourself? By using the psychofeedback technique, you will be able to get some answers that you can trust and use.

Exercise 1: Visual Feedback

Begin by sitting comfortably in a chair, feet flat on the floor. If you like, keep a pencil in one hand for taking notes, and put the other hand at your side. Take a couple of slow, deep breaths to relax, and put yourself in a receptive mood. You may wish to close your eyes, but this is not necessary. Some people are able to visualize with their eyes open. Try both ways to see which works better.

To prepare for this exercise, you'll start with two images: two crossed lines in the form of a large "X" and two perfectly parallel lines, "II."

First, in your mind's eye, picture a large "X." Picture it as if it represented where the treasure is buried on a treasure map. Look at it until it becomes very real and clear. Take a deep breath and then clear the picture from your mind. Next, say to your mind, "Show me the X." It should appear. When you see the X again, take a deep breath, let it out, and again clear the image.

Next, picture two parallel lines, "II." If it helps to imagine them as goal posts or the number eleven, do so. See the lines in your mind's eye. Take a deep breath, clear the image, and when you are ready, say to your mind, "Show me the parallel lines." They should appear. Breathe again and clear the picture.

You now have the two basic images in mind. When you want to find the answer to a question that is deep down inside, you'll begin the process by seeing a big X on the screen of your mind. Then, as you read or hear the question and repeat it simultaneously in your mind, if the answer is fundamentally "no," the X will remain. But if the answer is basically "yes," the X image will move apart and become parallel. This is an important part of the visual feedback process.

We all know that complicated emotional questions can rarely be answered with a simple "yes" or "no." In effect, the moving lines may position themselves automatically in some variation of a perfect X or perfectly straight parallel lines. This indicates mixed feelings, the predominant answer. You will occasionally notice at times, though, that the lines seem to move back and forth, indicating a very active thinking process with much uncertainty. Also, on occasion, the screen will suddenly go blank, indicating that your inner mind is fearful of revealing to your outer mind, the truth.

Your mind may then fear that you'll be frightened or seriously upset if it reveals this truth. You must take time, then, to develop a strategy that takes into account these fears—before this scary truth can be revealed. By and large, this will not be necessary because the act of doing these exercises sets up an "agreement" with your mind that you desire change and truth. Your mind is not likely to fail to cooperate.

Let's begin the visual feedback exercise. In your mind's eye, picture the big X. Now pose a question out loud. Repeat it over in your mind. Ask, "Deep down inside, is my name Albert Schweitzer?" The X should remain, unless by some amazing coincidence your name really is Albert Schweitzer. If it does not, continue working until you get used to the process. Allow at least several seconds for the image of the X to react. The more complex or emotionally laden the response, the more time it will take.

Now ask using your own name. Always begin deep down inside. Ask, "Deep down inside, is my name __________?" The lines should become parallel. Then ask, "Deep down inside, is my age 95?" It seems unlikely that you're 95, so the X should remain. Now plug in your own age and ask, "Deep down inside, is my age ___?" The lines should have become parallel.

To really get a feel for this method, continue with other simple questions like: "Deep down inside, do I live at ____________________________ (your correct address)?" "Deep down inside, is my job____________?" The correct answers should give you parallel lines.

Now let's try a more challenging question: "Deep down inside, do I feel I'm a good judge of character?" Your mind may give you different answers depending on what you think is involved in character. One of the things we learn about asking broad questions is that we get broad answers. It's important to be as precise and specific as possible.

Of course, you can't ask an overly detailed and long complex question either. Generally, your mind requires a question that's about a sentence in length. To the question of character judgment, you may want to merely note the answers that appear. Later, upon repeating these exercises, you may want to use the pencil to record the answers. You'll discover what is the best method for you. The important thing is that you get the correct information and know what to do with it.

Now that you understand the process, follow the questions below that deal with specific feelings. Remember, you're trying to find the feelings implied in the questions.

Visualizing Anger

This first section deals with hidden emotions—specifically, hidden anger. Begin with the intention of asking these questions at the deepest level of your mind.

Remember that every time you start a new question, begin with the X in place. When you've recorded the answer, take a deep breath, blow it out, and then reset the image of the X in your mind before asking the next question.

It's important to speak slowly—more slowly than you would in normal conversation. This is so your mind can take in the information, think about it carefully, and give you the right answer. If you speak too quickly, your mind will either think that you are not truly interested in getting the information, or it simply won't have time to process the answer.

Ask yourself the following questions and then record the answers as shown:

	X	II
1. Deep down inside, do I have unexpressed anger buried inside?	____	____
2. Deep down inside, am I secretly fearful of my anger? (Try to see what images appear.)	____	____
3. Deep down inside, do I feel I'll lose control of myself if I get angry?	____	____
4. Am I fearful that I will drive away my loved ones if I get angry?	____	____
5. Do I truly feel nice people shouldn't get angry?	____	____
6. Do I truly feel that if I get angry, I don't really love the person I'm angry at?	____	____
7. Does anger always lead to sorrow?	____	____
8. Deep down inside, do I really feel that friends and relatives will punish me if I get angry with them?	____	____

Here are several related questions. Each time you use a new word, clear out the old answer as quickly as possible.

9. Deep down inside, do I have hidden anger for my mother?	____	____
Father?	____	____
Sister?	____	____
Brother?	____	____
Child?	____	____

Spouse? ____ ____
A friend? ____ ____
Boss? ____ ____

10. Deep down inside, do I really feel that it's pointless to express anger—that it never does any good? ____ ____

Understanding Your Responses

You may be quite surprised at some of the answers that you have received. Even if you're fearful of some of them, it is very important that you know and accept your feelings. As we continue, we'll be asking deep questions. You want to enjoy learning to know yourself.

OTHER METHODS OF VISUAL FEEDBACK

Now that you understand a little bit of the concept of visual feedback using the X technique, I want to show you the versatility of the concept. I have tried to stress the importance of understanding the ideas rather than just rote learning, for then a whole gamut of techniques becomes available to you.

The Door Technique

Every sighted person has some capacity to visualize something in their mind. It is only a question of finding what that something is. One of the simplest images I've discovered is that of a door. Everyone has a door in their life. This door will now lead you to some further insights.

Just as before, you need to have a question you wish to have answered from deep down inside. Let's ask the question, "Am I willing to do whatever is necessary to help myself?" Imagine a door in front of you—any kind of a door. To begin, the door will be closed. Now when you ask the question, if the answer is basically "no" the door will remain closed; but if the answer to the question is basically "yes" then the door will begin to open. It might open just a crack or fling wide open. (See Figure 11.) The speed and the amount of the door opening is an indication of how true that statement is for you.

Figure 11

Let's try another question: "Deep down inside do I feel I have the respect of friends and relatives?" What happened to the door? Sometimes the door will open and close alternately. That often means the mind is confused by the question. Perhaps in your case your friends respect you, but your relatives don't.

Just for practice, let's ask one more question: "Deep down inside do I feel worthy to receive love exactly as I am?" Once again begin with the door closed and notice what happens to it when you ask yourself the question.

Variations on a theme

If you can't imagine a door, think of anything in your life that you can see. One lady in a group said she could only see the drawers in her dresser. I inquired whether it was filled with panties or bras. She replied that she could clearly see it was her panty drawer.

She was taken back a bit, I think, because it seemed so personal, but that is the point exactly. You see best what you know best. So if you don't like doors find a drawer. If you're more comfortable in the kitchen then imagine where the forks are kept.

Now find a drawer in your home and see it closed. Just as before, when the answer to the question is "no" the drawer will remain closed and when the answer is basically "yes" the drawer will open.

Let's ask this question: "Deep down inside do I in any way feel inadequate to help myself?" What happened to your drawer? Can you see what is happening here? What is in common with all these images? If you're starting to see a trend, it is this: If you can find an image of any object that you know well in your life and have it move back and forth or in and out, any kind of definite movement at all, and you know what it means, it will work. You can even use a made and unmade bed or a mixmaster turned on and off. It doesn't make any difference, it's just a symbol. In fact, your mind likes these little picture games. It is a form of exercise and, like your muscles, your mind likes to get worked out a bit too.

The X technique is still very valuable though, for as you will see it dovetails with methods of release in the chapters ahead and is invaluable in getting the energy flowing the way that you want. It is, however, just a picture and if you don't like it, pick another one.

MAKING PATTERNS

One concept of major importance throughout your entire program is the concept of a pattern. A pattern is, by definition, a statement that describes a bit of personal truth as you believe it, *deep down inside*. These patterns are the building blocks of your personal philosophy and work to create your life. A belief pattern that is true might be "Ultimately, I'll be treated by others the way that I have treated them," or "Love is the most powerful force there is." Generally, however, when patterns are discussed, I'll be referring to false ones.

Following are more questions that deal with a variety of feelings. You will see, as you go through this first section on anger, how you can make the questions to which you had a positive response into declarative statements of truth. These personal truths are what you are trying to gain from the inventory.

With practice, you will learn to easily write down your patterns. After a while, you will also be able to make patterns out of images. Patterns and images are to be used interchangeably. You will find that the ability to work with simple patterns will aid you greatly in focusing on things that bother you and that don't work in your life.

There are no exact rules as to how to make patterns from questions. Whenever you respond positively to a question, simply put it into a form that is short and sweet—a form that allows you to focus on the problem quickly but accurately. If possible, use the same words found in the question to make a statement about yourself. For example, the question, "Do I have unexpressed anger buried inside?" might become the statement, "I am fearful of the unexpressed anger buried inside me." The essence of the issue is unexpressed anger.

(Notice I chose to create the pattern using the word "fearful." I could have just as easily used "mistrustful" or "worried," but I chose fearful because it is more powerful and evokes the most emotional response.)

A positive response to the second question could be phrased simply as "I am fearful of my anger." Note that this statement might be considered to be both true and false—although it is true that you believe it, it is false in the sense that it is unnecessary and unhealthful to fear your anger. Therefore, this statement is classified as a false belief.

Question 3 could be restated as a declarative sentence in several different ways:

1. I *feel* that I will lose control of myself if I get angry.
2. I *fear* that I will lose control of myself if I get angry.
3. I *will* lose control of myself if I get angry.

Again, this is a false belief pattern because it is an unhealthy belief.

Question 4 could be phrased "I am fearful I will drive away my loved ones if I get angry." But it is more direct to say "I will drive my loved ones away if I get angry." This not only is more direct, but it implies the emotion rather than stating it specifically, which allows other feelings to surface. For example, you might also feel depressed or guilty if you drive your loved ones away.

Question 5 rephrased becomes "Nice people shouldn't get angry." Question 6 is stated as "If I get angry, I don't really love the person," or "When I get angry, I don't really love the person." Question 7 becomes "Anger always leads to sorrow." Although a few variations are possible such as "I feel that . . . " or "I know it is true that . . . ," it is more powerful when stated succinctly.

Really work with these patterns. Simply checking "positive" doesn't even begin to address the problem. These patterns are so deeply ingrained that until you can really feel them as statements of truth, change will be very difficult.

Look at Question 8: "Friends and relatives will punish me if I get angry with them." Is that a true statement? Is it healthier to live with this belief or without it?

Question 9 requires a slightly different treatment. The statement, "I have anger for my mother (or father)," is important to know and accept, but the greater issue is the implied value judgment that may go along with the statement. To make a useful pattern, it is necessary to fill in the implied judgment.

For example, the belief that it's immoral (or wrong or a sin) to be angry at your mother is at the heart of the issue. It may take some extra work to discover what special phrase works for you with respect to your mother or father. The psychofeedback questions will not cover every possibility, so you may have to dig a little to get the correct pattern, either on your own or with someone else.

Question 10 becomes "It's pointless to express anger. It never does any good." This is an extremely common belief pattern, and one many cancer patients believe too deeply.

LOOSENING UP TO FEEL YOUR THOUGHTS

Before getting into the experience of feeling your thoughts, it's important to loosen up a bit and allow the feelings to flow through. Loosening up here is not quite the same as what you do before exercising at the gym. You may be very limber and athletic and yet the muscles you need to feel your thoughts can be quite tight. We want to open up three major areas—the neck and shoulders, the jaw, and the pelvis—just a little.

Neck and Shoulders

The purpose of this exercise is to develop awareness. If you are too tight, you won't be able to sense any changes as your feelings rumble through your body. Begin with a simple head roll. Gently move your head and neck, forward and backward, slowly five or six times. The slower the better. Then make easy circles first to the left and then to the right five or six times. Take a couple of easy, relaxing, deep breaths and sense any feelings that come up before going on to the next part.

Now take a few seconds to become aware of your shoulders. Don't do anything yet. Do they feel tight? Are they down, low and relaxed or are they up higher, closer to your ears? When you are aware of where they are in space then shrug your shoulders—exaggerate the motion, hold them up towards your ears for a count of six, and then let them down slowly. Repeat this exercise four more times. Now stop, close your eyes, and sense your shoulders and neck. Become aware of yourself. While focusing on your neck and shoulders, take a breath just a little deeper than normal and notice how your neck and shoulders respond to that. When you are satisfied you have some greater sensitivity and feeling in your neck and shoulders, move on to the next exercise.

Opening the Jaw

Take a moment to sense the position of your jaw. Notice if you are biting down hard on your molars. Is there any space between your lips? Next, gently massage the jaw muscles about half an inch below the ears. Are they tight? Do you sometimes wake up in the morning with a sore jaw? Have you been told you grind your teeth? The jaw is a major key to holding in or releasing emotion. Now begin to move your jaw back and forth, first slowly then more rapidly about 10 or 15 times. Move it up and down again first slowly then quickly for about 15 seconds.

With your jaw a little relaxed and open just enough to put a tongue depressor in, think to yourself about something that you cannot do. Repeat to yourself something that's really true for you and say it with sincerity, "I can't do it. I can't do it. I just can't do it." Repeat the phrase five or six times. It may be something like, "I just can't make that call. I can't confront him/her. I just can't forgive them for what they've done to me."

Notice what happens to your jaw when you think those thoughts. If you've done it correctly, your jaw should be a little to a lot tighter. Think about what that feels like and continue on. Starting with your jaw in the neutral, slightly open position, say the phrases "I won't do it. I won't do it. You can't make me. I just won't do it." Once again your jaw is going to be a little tight—at the very least. Remember what that feels like. Once again relax your jaw so that it opens at least one quarter of an inch. Now this time, begin to slowly (then more rapidly) move your lower jaw up and down—a little like you are crying. Do that for about one minute. Then stop, rest, and sense how your jaw feels. Begin to move your lower jaw from side to side for about one minute. Now stop and once again sense the level of relaxation.

In the exercises to follow, notice how your jaw responds when you ask yourself questions; try to feel your thoughts. An automatic clenching of the jaw is your body telling you that this is an issue of deep feeling and probably something you are in conflict about deep down inside. The more relaxed your jaw is, the easier it is to sense these changes.

A Little Pelvis Action

Finally, let's open up the lower part of the body in a way that will enhance your sensitivity to feelings. Begin by moving your hips slowly around in a circle, first one way then the other. Do that for a couple of minutes moving to your right and left. Now place your hands on your hips and thrust your pelvis, first slowly then more quickly back and forth. Try to sense what feelings are there. The pelvis is one major source of control in the body and when you begin to move and stretch it, the hidden feelings will begin to surface. They may be erotic, anxious, or power feelings. Pay close attention to what comes up. When you are done, sense and remember what is there and proceed on to feeling your thoughts.

FEELING YOUR THOUGHTS

Because the mind and body are so closely linked, every emotionally charged thought is automatically received by the body. When you are able to feel precisely where a thought is troubling you, you can then effectively eliminate that thought. It is a simple exercise to truly feel all of your thoughts merely by asking your inner self to reveal them to you and by agreeing that you will gratefully experience whatever you feel.

Your inner mind is more than willing to give you any information that you request. It is your friend. The hard part is knowing what to do with it and ultimately accepting it as a part of yourself. Too quickly, you can shut off the flow of information, so it is best to keep an open mind to all that is revealed. After you have developed skill in using the questions here, you'll be able to devise your own. Very soon you'll be discovering your own issues and answers.

The ultimate goal is that you develop such an intimate relationship with your mind that your body will always tell you how you are doing or what you are thinking on any life issue. The technique of psychofeedback is meant to be a lifelong tool.

PROPER INTENTION

To begin, get comfortable in your seat, uncross your legs, place your feet flat on the floor, and close your eyes. Restate your intentions to your inner mind as follows:

> ***"I freely and willingly will allow all thoughts and beliefs, from deep down inside to be experienced in my body."***

Concentrate on the phrase. You're used to giving names to feelings like "mad," "sad," "glad," and so on, but these labels describe you only in a general way. The more precise and specific you are, the more you are in touch with what you feel deep down inside, and the more you'll be able to solve your problems.

You have already experienced little feelings many times but ignored them. The feelings I'm talking about are small contractions of muscles anywhere in your body. They are the twitches that suddenly begin and go away. They're also little pulsations, sticking or burning feelings, or a heavy feeling—a sense of tightness in one area or another. Sometimes people feel nauseous, trembly, or lightheaded. All of these are parts of the same expressions of the inner self.

You'll discover that every problem or illness that you have is associated with specific thought patterns as repeatable, small feelings. These patterns generally represent misunderstandings or false beliefs that have created turmoil or conflict. It is these specific, false belief patterns that you'll eliminate in order to achieve prosperity, eliminate headaches and ulcers, or improve almost any condition.

You are now ready to try the skill of *feeling your thoughts* in the area of anger. Go back to the 10 questions beginning on page 103.

After completing the section on anger, continue with fear. (You will learn new skills to deal with depression and guilt.)

FEAR

As you ask the following questions and feel your responses, don't be concerned with Xs or parallel lines (though if they appear, that's okay too). Then, as you ask yourself a question, note your response. As before, always think about these questions deep down inside.

	X	II
1. Do I have hidden fears that have not been expressed?	____	____
2. Do I sometimes fear things and don't know why?	____	____
3. Am I willing to do whatever is necessary to overcome my fears?	____	____
4. Do I secretly fear expressing my emotions honestly?	____	____
5. Deep down inside, do I fear confronting people that I need to?	____	____
6. Do I ever get so fearful that I actually panic?	____	____
7. Do I fear being revealed as a fraud or a phony?	____	____

8. Deep down inside, do I avoid letting people really know me for fear they will not like me? ____ ____

9. Deep down inside, am I fearful that one day I will be all alone—abandoned by everyone? ____ ____

10. Do I feel certain people will lose respect for me if I reveal my fears? ____ ____

11. Do I feel fear is the same as cowardice? ____ ____

12. Deep down inside, do I fear it's too late in my life to make the changes I really desire? ____ ____

Understanding Your Responses

You should now know how to generate a pattern. Remember, a pattern is simply a specific statement about a bit of your life philosophy. Some of the preceding questions will fit directly into a pattern and some will not. The first question, for example, does not.

Question 1, which simply affirms that you have hidden fears, is too general. To create a meaningful pattern, you need to specify which fear. A useful pattern statement might be "I have hidden fears that I have not expressed about air travel." The fear could be something about which you are already aware, or it might be necessary to track down your fears using the X-II process.

Question 2 leads to an informative statement, but it is not a specific false belief pattern. Most of us have things we fear but don't know why. The question really is how honest will you be with yourself and how deep will you dig?

Question 4, by contrast, is a pretty straightforward false belief. You know that you must express yourself. Question 5 is also fairly clear and very common. Simply stated it is, "I fear confronting people whom I need to confront." You can further specify it by adding "because they will leave me (or hate me)," or whatever you feel will happen.

FEELING YOUR BREATH

Besides using your "mind's eye" and whole body to answer deep questions, you can use your lungs as well. It's important to understand a general rule about your mind-body connection. The rule is that any questions you ask yourself will be answered someplace in your body. Any questions of *any* significance regarding love, work, friendship—any part of your life at all—are all registered in your body. One of the most accessible and reliable places to register a response is in your chest.

Let's take the earlier example: "Do I feel I am a good judge of character?" Suppose the answer was fuzzy or you got an answer opposite to what you consciously thought. You now simply repeat the question in the usual way, but this time closely observe the ease of your breathing. If you're very clear on the issue, when you inhale or exhale, it will be easy or natural. If, however, you are doubtful in any way or find that your conscious answer is different from your unconscious one, you will find a little catch in your breathing. It may hold or stick a little or be completely blocked with no air entering or leaving for just a moment. This will depend, of course, upon how concerned you are about the issue.

Whenever a question catches or locks in your chest, it is a confirmation that the question represents a problem or a conflict that you are working on. The catch in your breathing is very important. Your inability to breathe freely represents a serious stress point that is deeply imbedded in your mind. You cannot expect to be truly healthy and well if your breath does not flow.

As you become aware of the various other parts of your body, such as your back, jaw, and shoulder, you'll readily see that they too contract or constrict with certain questions. For now, use your breathing to answer the questions until the technique is comfortable and natural in your mind. Don't forget to make notations of those that you need to work on further.

Remember, as you hear the questions in your mind, put all your attention on your breathing. You'll be able to notice the slightest variations with each and every question. Even with your attention on your breathing, you may still find the X or parallel lines appearing because now you have learned the technique. If so, they will simply confirm to you the importance of the question and the issues at hand. If you find that your mind doesn't show you very much as you're focusing on your breathing, don't be too concerned. After a while, like driving a car, you'll be able to do many things simultaneously.

DEPRESSION

Depressive false beliefs present a slightly different wrinkle to making patterns. Much of depression is dependent on repeating pessimistic statements to yourself about the way the world seems to be. Many questions in this section, then, are confrontative and ask you how or why you think as you do. As you try to answer, you will find the deeper belief that lies within.

	X	II
1. Deep down inside, am I more depressed than I tell others?	____	____
2. Deep down inside, do I feel that life has let me down?	____	____
3. Do I really feel that I've been a failure in life?	____	____
4. Would the world be better off without me?	____	____
5. Deep down inside, do I really feel that I'm not as good as other people?	____	____
6. Have I gone along for years not caring whether I lived or died?	____	____
7. Deep down inside, have I forgotten what it's like to feel happy?	____	____
8. Has life lost its purpose or meaning?	____	____
9. Do I feel that death would be a pleasant rest from all my suffering?	____	____
10. Deep down inside, do I secretly wish everyone would just leave me alone and not try to be so helpful?	____	____

Did you sense changes in your breathing? Could you sense where there was a block while breathing in or out? Repeat those questions where you felt blocked and sense the feelings in the rest of your body.

Understanding Your Responses

In response to unhappiness, pain, fear, and anger, the natural reaction is to pull into ourselves. The body also contracts when one part believes one way and the other part believes the opposite. For example, if you are feeling depressed and worthless or think of yourself in terms of failure, it automatically means that you are holding back feelings of sadness. This sadness is reflected in the body as tension in your cheeks and in the muscles around your eyes and lips. There may be some tightening of the throat as well.

Perhaps the most noticeable area of tension is the jaw. We use our jaw in three major ways:

- *To hold back tears when we are sad*
- *To hold in verbal expression when we are angry*
- *To freeze and tighten against our fears and anxieties as a defensive mechanism.*

The other areas of the body—shoulders, chest, back, and pelvis—have similar patterns of contraction as well, depending on what we are protecting ourselves against.

At some level you are always pushing and pulling *against yourself* to keep your true feelings inside. Squeezing and tightening sensations are your best attempts to hold yourself together. The only exception is that at times some people are very ready to let everything loose as they experience the relief of letting the truth come out. After you practice feeling your thoughts and noticing what your body does when you think or feel deeply about a particular sentence or memory, it will seem clearer that these feelings want to get out.

As you become more comfortable with communicating with yourself, *expecting* to feel your feelings, the visual feedback and the breathing will seem part of the same feedback process. No longer are they individual exercises, but an integrated system of self-awareness—of the changing moods and feelings that lie within.

As in the other exercises, it is a good idea to go over the questions and try to make some sense of your responses apart from your feelings. For example, if you are feeling that you don't belong in the world or can't find much purpose in life, it is imperative that you find someone to talk to about these feelings. It is natural to feel low or in despair at times as we suffer losses of one kind or another. But when we can no longer see how we fit in or don't feel connected to anything or anyone, it is time for some soul searching. Look over your responses and the implications and decide before you go further that you are seriously going to work this out yourself or you will get some help right away.

Question 1 asks "Are you truly more depressed than you tell others?" If your answer is yes, you need to examine why it is so. Begin to acknowledge it by saying, "I am more depressed than I tell others because nobody really cares," or "I'll make them feel bad," or "Other people's problems are more important than mine." Discover the second part to this statement and find someone with whom to discuss it. Remember, it is a false belief to think you must hide your feelings from others.

In the same fashion, Questions 2 and 3 also express personal opinions that need to be explored. As in Question 1, they can be made specific by adding a second part, the hidden part. If you feel that the world would be better off without you, you obviously cannot expect to be very well, mentally or physically. Such a belief is unhealthy for both the individual and society. We must believe in ourselves if we are to make the world a better place in which to live.

This leads to Question 5 which translates into "I feel I'm not as good as other people." It should be obvious to you that this is false. In fact, the system doesn't even recognize the concept of better or worse people. People just *are*, and they try in their own way to be well and happy. This belief, however, is very common, and you should be prepared to work hard to correct it if you want to be well. I repeat: *You cannot walk around thinking that other people are better than you and expect to be optimally well.*

For the remainder of the questions, set up the declarative statement and add endings that are appropriate for you.

You've now practiced three techniques for getting feedback about your false beliefs. In the guilt questions that follow, use first one technique and then another, and compare the outcomes. Regardless of which technique you use, you should be able to identify your feelings deep down inside.

GUILT

Now let's practice one more general emotion that many people feel: guilt. Focus primarily on the feelings, and notice whether they're in your head, chest, belly, or even at the tips of your toes.

	X	II
1. Do I still feel guilty for things I have said or done in the past?	____	____
2. Has guilt affected important decisions in my life?	____	____
3. Do I have hidden guilt concerning mother?	____	____
Father?	____	____
Sister?	____	____
Brother?	____	____
Child?	____	____
Spouse?	____	____
A friend?	____	____
A stranger?	____	____

4. Am I willing to do *whatever* is necessary to relieve my guilt? ____ ____

5. Would I rather die than reveal certain things that I've said or done? ____ ____

6. Do I sometimes feel guilty and angry at the same time? ____ ____

7. Do I feel I suffer now for the pain I have caused others? ____ ____

8. Do I feel that guilty feelings and my illness are related? ____ ____

Take a moment to collect your thoughts and note what feelings you've experienced. Little twitches? Tightening in certain areas? You've been very honest with yourself, and that's the first step in making the changes you desire.

Understanding Your Responses

Guilt is different in terms of belief patterns than fear or anger because most people are well aware of their feelings of guilt. The problem is they can't or won't get rid of them. The issue, then, is not to uncover the false belief but to come to the understanding that it is neither necessary nor useful to feel guilty.

This isn't to say that you shouldn't feel badly if you truly hurt someone. The appropriate response would be to acknowledge your wrongdoing and then let it go. Continuing to punish yourself over past misdeeds is pointless. The sad truth is, however, that most people feel guilty about imagined events or things over which they have no control rather than actual misdeeds, which makes their guilt even more inappropriate.

Notice that Questions 1 through 3 are designed to start you thinking about the guilt in your life. Question 3, in particular, allows for different endings to give you something to work with. For example, "I have hidden guilt feelings about my mother because I left the hospital angry and she died shortly thereafter." People always feel guilty *about something,* so add the appropriate ending that applies to you.

Question 7 is a general one that presents a more obvious pattern; some of the others are good for thought and discussion. After completing the exercise, continue to work on your feelings of guilt by writing down the specifics about those things that still make you feel guilty. Then, following the examples below, rewrite them to reflect a healthier perspective. Make a commitment to release all of your remaining guilt feelings.

Examples

1. I felt I let Mother down, but now I know I did my best.
2. I thought Father died because I didn't get there on time, but now I know it would have made no difference.
3. I should have realized that my son was using drugs, but I realize now that I acted correctly with the knowledge I had.

Complete these statements about your own issues:

1. I felt. . .
2. I should have. . .

LOVE

We have covered some issues in the four most basic negative emotions. It is now time to look at love. The word means so many different things to different people that at times it seems to have lost its meaning. Included in the idea of love is romance, friendships, family, and religion, to name only a few.

The following questions will have a romantic slant, but they acknowledge that concerns exist in all of the love areas, and each carries equal importance.

Deep down inside. . .

	X	II
1. Do I believe that there is anyone who will ever love me as I desire?	____	____
2. Is great sex a sure sign of love?	____	____
3. Does love mean giving up my independence?	____	____
4. Does the man/woman have the advantage in a love relationship?	____	____
5. Have I avoided love because of the fear of the eventual pain it would bring?	____	____
6. Do I feel worthy enough to receive love?	____	____
7. Do I fear repeating my parents' love experience in my life?	____	____
8. Have I been repeating my parents' love experience in my life?	____	____
9. Does falling in love feel like being out of control?	____	____
10. Is it foolish to believe that romantic love ever really works out?	____	____

If one of the many expressions of love is an issue and you are not sure how you feel or perhaps why you experience things as you do, write down your own questions about love. Use the X and parallel lines as the feeling method, and find out what is going on deep down inside.

STILL MORE ISSUES

To demonstrate the kinds of questions that can be asked and how diverse they can be, look at the following *deep down inside.*

Worthiness and Self-Esteem

1. Does someone have to be worthy to be loved?
2. Has my sense of worth been affected by mother?
   Father?
   Sister?
   Brother?
   Friend?
   Teacher?
3. Do I feel less than others and don't know why?
4. Do I feel the need to be or do something special to have (feel) more self-worth?
5. Do I feel I have to be perfect or feel like I have failed?

Success

1. Do I feel that if I get a more responsible position, they may discover I'm incompetent?
2. Do I feel that making or having a lot of money is bad or corrupting in some way?
3. Do I feel the only way I can be acknowledged by others is to be a success?
4. Do I fear the responsibilities that success or promotion will bring?
5. Is there a part of me that still believes I'll never amount to anything?

Obviously, there are many other questions to be asked. Now it is your turn to find those false belief patterns. If you have not already done so, work with these and other patterns that you are preparing for release.

You've experienced and practiced different ways of receiving information (feedback) from yourself. Each one has its value, but the kinesthetic or "feeling" way is truly the most powerful. By learning to ask yourself questions and precisely experiencing *what* and *where* your feelings are, you'll be able to determine which thoughts and beliefs create which problems. So, if part of your body experiences a small sensation or discomfort in response to a troubling thought, it is a signal that you may need to work out and resolve this troubling thought. Otherwise, that "little" sensation might grow into a big disease, if it hasn't already.

It will always help to confirm your suspicions and sometimes to initially gain information by using the visual feedback techniques of imagining the X and parallel lines. After a while, you'll discover that you simultaneously see with your mind and feel with your body as you release the negative emotions handled by these patterns. If you don't "feel" a lot or "see" as well as you'd like, don't be discouraged. All learning takes time. If you don't feel much, you may be too anesthetized or sleepy from the habit of ignoring your body's responses. Go back to some of the earlier exercises in this book to wake up your body.

LOOKING AT ILLNESS

In this section we will be asking questions specifically for those individuals who have a physical or emotional illness with which they are actively working. The following questions are especially challenging, but don't be deterred; they are also the most enlightening. Go slowly, do your best, and if it seems your feelings are in a jumble, you will sort them out. Remember that some of the questions are at the very crux of what is the mind-body connection.

If you have a serious physical illness, use this opportunity to take a good, hard look at your personal belief system in relation to it. Upon completing the section, continue to create patterns in the same way as before.

	X	II
1. Did I always feel I would get this illness?	____	____
2. Is this illness a way of punishing myself for the way I have been in life?	____	____
3. Do I really desire to fight this condition with everything I have?	____	____
4. Was I depressed for a long time before this illness appeared?	____	____
5. Is this illness my chance to leave an unpleasant life?	____	____
6. Am I secretly relieved that I now have this illness?	____	____
7. Do I feel that stress played any part in the creation of this illness?	____	____
8. Do I know specific events or periods of time that contributed to my illness?	____	____
9. Am I willing to examine any relevant emotional factors in my illness?	____	____
10. Do I feel any of the following people in any way contributed to the creation of my illness?		
Mother?	____	____
Father?	____	____
Sister?	____	____

Brother? ____ ____
Spouse? ____ ____
Significant other? ____ ____
Friend? ____ ____
Children? ____ ____
Boss? ____ ____
Other? ____ ____

11. Do I feel any of the following people currently contribute to the maintenance of my illness?

Mother? ____ ____
Father? ____ ____
Sister? ____ ____
Brother? ____ ____
Spouse? ____ ____
Significant other? ____ ____
Friend? ____ ____
Children? ____ ____
Boss? ____ ____
Other? ____ ____

12. Do I feel that guilty feelings and my illness are related? ____ ____

13. If I feel guilty about something, does my illness flare up? ____ ____

14. Is my illness a punishment for things I've done or said? ____ ____

15. Did anyone ever predict that I might get this illness? ____ ____

16. Does God punish people by making them ill? ____ ____

17. Do I feel this illness is in any way related to hidden anger or hatred? ____ ____

18. Is this illness related to sexual wrongdoing? ____ ____

19. Am I willing to do or say anything necessary to get well? ____ ____

20. Do I secretly enjoy all the attention I'm now getting? ____ ____

21. Am I afraid that if I get well, things will be just as before? ____ ____

22. Have I waited for the attention I now get all of my life? ____ ____

23. Is my illness the only way to get the love I desire? ____ ____

24. Do my doctors often treat me like a child? ____ ____

25. Am I certain my doctors are telling me the whole truth? ____ ____

26. Do I avoid confronting my doctors for fear they might take it out on me somehow? ____ ____

27. If I use imagery to get well, will my doctors lose respect for me? ____ ____

28. Is my doctor's opinion of me more important than my opinion of myself? ____ ____

29. Do I feel my doctor tries to control me? ____ ____

30. Do I feel my doctor understands my suffering? ____ ____

31. Do I often feel like a burden to the family? ____ ____

32. Do I feel my family would rather I die as quickly as possible? ____ ____

33. If it would help my illness, would I tell my deepest or most painful feelings to

Mother? ____ ____
Father? ____ ____
Sister? ____ ____
Brother? ____ ____
Spouse? ____ ____
Friend? ____ ____
Children? ____ ____

34. Do I secretly feel like a martyr? ____ ____

35. If I were more certain there was an afterlife, would I fight my illness less? ____ ____

36. Do I fight to stay alive more for my family than myself? ____ ____

37. Do I ever feel guilty that I'm abandoning my family if I die? ____ ____

38. Do I wish there were someone I could really talk to about my feelings? ____ ____

39. Have people treated me differently than I expected since this illness? ____ ____

40. Did I find out I have friends that I didn't know I had? ____ ____

Understanding Your Responses

Some of these are actual false belief patterns to be removed, whereas others are intended more to stimulate thought or discussion.

This section deals frankly with questions that no one would ever ask you because they are embarrassing or considered to be too personal. It is particularly useful in this section if you can feel your answers *deep down inside*. In order to do that effectively, you must try not to use your conscious mind to answer, for the conscious mind tends to obscure the truth in order to protect the status quo. Your body, however, cannot lie. A truthful response, if it is disturbing in any way, naturally causes your body to become activated. Let your body answer, and you will know that this deeper mind, of which I have so often spoken, does exist.

PAINFUL FACTS

Something that you will find as you go deeper and deeper into yourself is that there are more and more painful areas that you have avoided or ignored. Much of your life has been spent avoiding these inner pains, but it has not served you well. As you have probably discovered by reading this book, it is sometimes necessary to stay with a painful part for a few seconds. Don't be discouraged by the possibility of some discomfort. The benefits experienced are enormous. Know and believe now that it will be worth your trouble, and, in the end, you will feel a tremendous sense of relief.

Having responded physically, begin to address those key issues with your family, your doctor, or others you may choose to help you. Let no stone go unturned in your search for healing. Know the truth, and it will free you to be well.

CHAPTER 10

THE POWER AND IMPORTANCE OF BELIEFS

In this chapter you will learn more about what constitutes a belief in order to understand when a belief is false.

By identifying what I call *false belief patterns* and releasing their unhealthy emotional charge, it is possible to heal and transform ourselves in many ways. To see how this might be possible, let us look in depth at the concepts of beliefs and patterns.

BELIEFS AND BELIEF SYSTEMS

Merely by reading this book, you will have greatly expanded your belief system. Even if you don't accept everything I say 100%, acknowledging some new possibilities makes inroads in your belief structure.

For example, in order to begin even to *think* of using the techniques described here, you have to believe that someone, somewhere has used them successfully. You must, in effect, believe that the knowledge exists before you can expect to use it. Reading these pages implies that you at least believe that such knowledge exists. Don't think lightly of the accomplishment either, for there are many intelligent, educated people who refuse to even read or try a different belief system. They are too threatened by an expanded world and a larger truth.

Beliefs, then, act as a key to open the door to a new world of knowledge, such as ways to control your body and access your unconscious mind. So, for example, if you're willing to try to visualize different colors in various portions of your body to help you heal, and you found that it works, this success would enhance your beliefs and encourage you to continue trying with greater enthusiasm. If you continue to study, practice, and refine the same basic belief, then soon your success will be greater, and you will believe even more deeply.

Beliefs accomplish a couple of things. Belief itself increases the likelihood of your success. The increased belief adds power to the practice and is superior to simply performing an exercise objectively. The desire generated by believers can make something succeed where neutral but compliant nonbelievers may not. This fact is often forgotten or misunderstood, but the belief itself is an intrinsic part of the practice, and it cannot be easily separated from the "objective" studies.

THE PLACEBO EFFECT

The fact that beliefs have real power is demonstrated by the so-called placebo effect. The placebo is a dummy, a fake treatment, usually a sugar pill. The placebo effect is both positive and negative. If you give patients dummy pills and warn them of the side effects, some of them will think they feel these effects even though there is no medical or scientific reason for it. Their belief is enough to convince them. That is the negative placebo effect.

On the positive side, you can give patients certain drugs and tell them what benefit to expect, and often as much as a third will respond positively when given the sugar pills. Essentially, this happens because they believe in the medicine or the doctor. This is especially true for treatments using pain pills, because pain is very responsive to beliefs and feelings.

The truth is that belief, either positive or negative, cannot be truly eliminated. For some types of treatments, belief is a helpful adjunct to the treatment. Belief is not static but, rather, part of the message. It is a common experience for cancer patients receiving chemotherapy to tolerate the medication better and perhaps to respond more favorably when they believe that the treatment is going to work and when they have confidence in their physician. It is vital that you believe in the treatment, no matter what it is.

I have spoken to many people given up for dead by conventional medicine who recovered from diseases such as cancer in very unorthodox and seemingly unbelievable ways. After studying this phenomenon, I am convinced that some people could be cured of a fatal illness with tap water. In fact, a very famous case substantiated this theory some thirty years ago at the University of Chicago, when a caring but misguided physician, Dr. Andrew Ivey, injected sterile water into a patient. As a result of the injection, the patient's cancer went into remission.

Somehow the newspapers got a hold of the story and printed it. After reading the article, the patient relapsed and was again injected with a "new, improved medication" by this doctor; and once again went into remission. He did well until the fraud was exposed and the doctor publicly disgraced. The patient died shortly thereafter.

In fact, most people probably would not have responded to a tap water treatment. Medical researchers are still trying to figure out who responds favorably in this way and why. The point is that this knowledge gives us the inspiration to search more deeply for the answers.

DECIDING WHAT TO BELIEVE

If you clearly understand that beliefs are not predominantly mental thoughts but well-blended, complete thoughts, then you can better understand why beliefs and images have power. The strongest belief of all—the belief in your own life, the desire to live—has been amply demonstrated to produce remarkable feats of strength and endurance. It seems logical, then, that deep belief in your fears robs you of strength and creates illness and suffering. Removal of these deeply believed fears would benefit you, for, as in all things in this life, that which you deeply believe is much more likely to come true than that for which you do not have much desire or belief. Belief energizes your effort. The belief is an intrinsic part of the whole process. The desire, including the desire to be well, which is one of the most powerful desires of all, should be used not eliminated.

Because beliefs are both mental and emotional, like all thoughts, some people believe things because they are logically based, and some believe them because primarily they are emotionally appealing. The best, of course, is when both parts are present and accurately represent reality, but this is not always the case.

The fault lies in the belief that your personal experience, or even that of a small group, constitutes the greater, more accurate reality. Almost everyone, until he or she learns better, believes that his or her world-view is correct because of his or her experiences. *Airplanes are dangerous, short men are liars, and gypsies are thieves.* Whatever you choose to believe, it will appear logical, rational, and emotionally satisfying if your experience has verified that belief for you.

"REALITY" AND FALSE BELIEFS

In our psychoenergetic system model, you do not use your own *reality* to define your beliefs. Instead, you must base your beliefs on a more universal reality, one that may even contradict your personal reality. If you are to progress now, you must understand several important things about beliefs.

1. There is a greater reality more accurate than your own.

2. Your problems may, in fact, stem from your persistent lack of experience or appreciation of this reality.

3. You are probably not cognizant of the beliefs that form your world-view and therefore tend to believe your conscious mind instead of the more powerful and accurate unconscious mind.

If you've gotten this far in the book, you have discovered, that unless you dig deep down inside, you'll find it hard to know what you truly think and feel. The average person never challenges his or her own beliefs until he or she encounters a big problem. Do you have a big problem? Are you challenging your previously held beliefs to see if they conform to a greater reality?

Put this idea in the front of your mind now: You must begin to believe and accept that your beliefs are probably unknown to you, often contradictory, and frequently false. A lot of your beliefs exist because they either feel right or appear logical, but they are not accurate. In fact, if you ask people why they do what they do, often they will say they don't know. The majority of your beliefs are basically logical and functional, or you wouldn't have come this far in life; but that is not far enough to achieve the health you desire. Now you must go farther.

Part of the secret to going farther is to examine and challenge your beliefs. For the most part, the beliefs I discuss concern your emotions. If you are not in touch with your anger, sadness, fear, doubt, and so on, and if you don't know what you feel and believe about the important people in your life and life choices that you have made, then you cannot be truly well. Your beliefs on these subjects are simply too critical in the creation of your lifestyle to be casually accepted without serious study. The beliefs found to be faulty, unproductive, and harmful must be removed. Accordingly, the first step entails further study about the true nature of beliefs.

BELIEFS, OPINIONS, AND INTENSITY

A belief is an opinion that quantitatively and qualitatively describes the amount of truth you assign to real or imagined experiences or ideas.

The intensity of the experience is related to the feelings generated when reexperiencing the memories associated with the beliefs. Keep in mind this intensity factor when you reexperience or discharge feelings, because it tells you about the feelings locked deep inside and how hard you may need to work to release them. Recall that these beliefs are nothing more than opinions. These opinions often seem to be the truth or reality, but the apparent truth does not change the fact that it is still your opinion. Your goal, then, is to align yourself with the more universally accurate opinion, if there is one. It may not always be easy to decide which is the most accurate opinion to hold; in fact, it can be quite challenging to find the *universal opinion.*

UNIVERSAL OPINION

The universal opinion or universal reality is really about promoting the ideal. To understand this better, suppose your life has been filled with abandonment, rejection, and abuse. Practically speaking, that is what lies deep down inside—your personal truth. The universal reality—the ideal—is the belief in the goodness of mankind.

As you begin to release unwanted, painful energies, you must first acknowledge completely your personal truth. Nothing about it can be denied. After that, however, in order to completely release it, you must at least momentarily believe in the opposite—the ideal—in order to free it from yourself. It is not excusing another person's behavior to hold these beliefs.

A benefit of beginning to believe in the ideal has to do with the magnetic property of beliefs. Beliefs as energy systems follow certain laws. The law on the emotional level is that like beliefs attract each other. That simply means that loving beliefs find and attract other loving beliefs.

Turning your beliefs toward the ideal is the hardest part of the healing process. If you can say to yourself, "I know what's been, but I also know what can be," the rest will seem easy. Try to think how love begets love, trust begets trust, and so on.

BELIEF OR TRUTH

What does it mean when you say that you "believe" something? Remember that beliefs are common ideas melded together in a consistent pattern. Beliefs organize the world around you and make it understandable. I invite you to abandon the idea that you already know what you believe and have fun discovering your true beliefs. Think for a moment how you use the word *belief*. You take for granted many ideas that you don't really consider as beliefs; they seem to be truths or common understandings.

Consider the belief found in the question, "Do you believe in love?" You might reply, "What's to believe or not? Love just seems to exist." Likewise, if I were to inquire whether you believe in working for a living, you might also reply, "Well, of course. I can't afford not to believe in it."

But if I asked whether you believed that the primary purpose of work is to make money or achieve life satisfaction, there are going to be some differences of opinion about what might be called the work ethic. There is a difference in the flavor of the word *belief* as it is used to describe work versus love. In time you will see that everything you think, do, or feel reflects a belief, a real choice that you have made, not a given. This will become clearer as you continue.

The groupings of beliefs that seem to consistently fit together are referred to as a *belief system.* A belief system organizes your behavior so it seems that you are consistent with your actions. Beliefs in groupings of systems can be very simple or complex. Awareness has much to do with looking at your beliefs as they exist in a system and reasoning which ones do not fit smoothly together and thereby cause conflict. Conflicting beliefs, along with incorrect beliefs standing alone, are a major cause of "problems" and distress in your life.

When our actions contradict our words it is because we do not understand unconscious beliefs; we are living in the world of illusion. And as long as we live in the world of illusion, we have difficulty creating the *reality* of the life that we desire.

Every aspect of your life—your job, your family, your marriage, how you play games, or use deodorant—represents different belief systems. To the extent that these larger groupings of beliefs are altogether consistent, this consistency is a clear reality, versus that of conflict and illusion. Your goal, then, is not only to remove false beliefs but also to search for inconsistencies, conflicts within specific belief systems, as well as how well the belief systems mesh.

The more you work on beliefs, the more you will notice that each belief is underlaid by an even more fundamental one, a *core belief.* Sometimes early memories are mistaken for core beliefs because they initiated a behavior that continues to exist in the present. The belief is really the decision, the one-sentence conclusion. Such beliefs—for example, "I am evil or worthless" or "I will always be abandoned"—are core beliefs. To the extent possible, finding the memory is always helpful, but the core belief itself is what you are really after, and often it is not easily associated with a memory you can recall. Try to discover for yourself the difference between a core belief and a more general one.

CHOOSING BELIEF-MAKING OPINIONS

Let's do an exercise for the next couple of minutes. After reading this section, put the book down and consider some of your beliefs about God and religion. Consider God and His relationship to people (if any) and how your religious training taught or related these concepts.

While you are considering that, think about how you derived your beliefs. Did they come from your mother, father, a teacher, readings, or specific experiences? Think about the people closest to you. Do you know where their beliefs originated? Consider how well their belief systems work for them. Are they better off for believing what they do in a demonstrable way? Can you see how their beliefs affect their lives?

Consider marriage, work, happiness—any belief system held by your family and friends. Do their beliefs make the world seem a better place? Finally, think about whether you would like to believe something different from what you do, if that were possible. You might find that you believe things that you would rather not, such as a resentment or bias against another ethnic group. You don't even know how you formed these opinions.

In your search for clarity and direction as to what to believe, it is often valuable to consider how the beliefs came to be in order to determine whether or not you really want to keep the ones you have or change them somewhat. A good way to practice being open to change is by pretending to hold beliefs that differ from the ones you actually hold. By doing so, you begin to see the world through different eyes. You experience yourself in new and different ways and realize that you are more flexible than you thought.

BELIEFS TO HAVE AND TO HOLD

Let's suppose that you have a serious health problem and believe that God is punishing you for something you have done. How will this affect your ability to get well? Does it make any difference how hard you try? What can you really do to help yourself?

Now let's pretend you believe that God is loving and merciful and you don't believe that you are being punished at all. You believe that God helps those who help themselves. How do these beliefs affect your ability to fight your illness? Can you see how your beliefs or opinions in this area might affect the outcome?

Suppose you were sick and did not know what you believed deep down inside. Would finding out make any difference? Would you choose to hold different beliefs, if you could?

Now that you know why I stress the importance of knowing your beliefs, let's begin to remove the ones we don't want by following the techniques in the next chapter.

CHAPTER 11

RELEASING FALSE BELIEF PATTERNS

You are now ready to begin removing patterns that you have learned to detect from using exercises earlier in this book.

From the patterns, which consist of a mental part (specific words) and a feeling part (the emotional charge), we will work to remove the uncomfortable feeling state—anger, fear, guilt, hatred, and so on. Removing the emotion results in an alteration in the belief in the words that are left. Let's begin with an explanation of the various techniques.

TECHNIQUE 1: Activation By Repetition

Begin with a pattern or belief. Let's say, for example, you discovered that deep down inside, you feel unworthy because you feel that no one loves you. This pattern is expressed as "I feel worthless if nobody loves me."

While sitting in the neutral position, or lying on a bed, repeat your pattern out loud five or six times. After the fifth or sixth repetition, you should start to experience the feelings that are attached to those words. Say how you feel ("I'm worthless" or "I feel so worthless") 15 to 20 times. Remember to say the words sincerely; in other words, when you say, "I feel angry," sound angry. Rushing through the feelings or saying them blandly or neutrally won't be effective.

Allow the feelings to come through—don't attempt to obstruct or suppress them. You may notice heat, sweating, trembling, or shaking. You may also experience nausea or gagging. You may feel little twitches or tightness in one or more places. You also may begin to clench your jaw or tighten your thighs. Coughing especially is a sure sign that you are deep into the pattern.

After you have repeated all or part of the pattern 12 to 15 times, say the following:

> ***"I acknowledge this false belief about feeling worthless because nobody loves me, and I am willing to release it now. I am releasing this foolish and false belief."***

Repetition of the entire pattern will increase its effectiveness. Repeat the word "releasing," and the process will continue. If you feel energy being released, don't try to stop it. As you continue to repeat the feeling phrase "I'm worthless," several more things will happen.

First, as the emotions build, your breathing may increase until you are almost panting from agitation. Then, over the next 4 to 10 minutes your emotions will seem to have run dry, and you will find yourself saying the words without much feeling. This is a sign that a lot of the discomfort has passed, and you will feel a sense of relief that something has been lifted from you.

GOING DEEPER

Repeating the phrase allows the feeling to come out until it runs dry. Another avenue for the feeling is to use the words that appear in your mind that are associated with the feeling of worthlessness, or whatever emotion you used in the exercise above. For example, associated with "I feel worthless" could be thoughts such as "because of them. . . they told me I could never do it. . . . I hate what they did to me." Some of the statements that come to your mind may surprise you, but allow whatever thoughts or ideas that pop into your head to complete the phrase that began "I feel worthless."

You then can use the next words you hear, "They told me I could never do it," and repeat them three or four times. Continue to repeat "I could never do it" over and over again allowing the feelings to surface. There may be tears, anger, hatred—all kinds of feelings will be layered one upon the other. First there may be anger, then sadness, then more anger. Another time there may be a feeling of guilt and, underneath, more anger.

Now use the next spontaneous phrase, repeating it 10 to 20 times, staying with it, being open, and allowing the feelings to surface, which they naturally will. Repeat the phrase with sincerity, and emotions will come up. *Do not judge it in any way. Give total acceptance to it.* You may be amazed by the intensity of your feelings. As you continue to say the phrase, you will release the emotional part of the pattern. It actually begins to diminish on its own.

Afterwards you will notice that you feel calmer, freer. Perhaps the sick feeling in the pit of your stomach, or the heaviness in your chest or shoulders, is gone. There may be new lightness to the feeling around your eyes and mouth. Any and all parts of your body may be affected, according to what was first stimulated. When you ask yourself "How worthless do I feel now?" you will find that you have changed somewhat, though you may not be able to put your finger on it.

The emotion, as you will see, is not a continuous state of bad feeling, but rather like clusters or packets that clear, at least momentarily, and then begin again. The release of each energy packet helps to weaken the false belief pattern. There are several ways to sense if you are, in fact, releasing much energy through your exercises. Energy released can be experienced by:

1. increased sweating on the forehead, chest, or palms,
2. a sudden rush of pleasant warmth, as well as a burning or tingling sensation,
3. coughing, often with a honking sound, yawning, sneezing, and tearing,
4. a sensation of gagging or nausea, which rapidly clears,
5. minor trembling in the limbs, or
6. a sudden sense of fatigue or sudden energy spurt.

Any and all of these may be experienced in addition to the sensations of anger, guilt, fear, and so on.

You will experience that the primary belief or pattern is held in place by the emotions. As you discharge the emotions, the pattern is weakened, and you won't find it quite so believable. The feelings will also frequently stir up memories, and it is important to get into those memories at some point. However, because they can distract you from your purpose, first complete the feeling exercise. Then, at a later date, after you have calmed down, go back to the memories and see if you can use them as another stimulus to generate more feelings.

It is vitally important that you understand that the repetition of a very negative phrase such as "I'm worthless," "I'm angry," "I hate you," or even "I'll kill you" does not reinforce these tendencies, as some might believe. Rather, repetition actually acts to *discharge* the feelings when the *intention* to do so is there. If, however, you don't intend it, and you don't expect and desire to release it, then there could be a tendency to reinforce the prevailing pattern. So it is important to be clear in your own mind that you are saying these things with sincerity and feeling, as a method of discharge. With a little practice, you will be able to split your mind in such a way that part of you feels everything and clears out false beliefs while another part observes and sees the intensity of emotion as a curious or interesting thing.

Practice Session for Technique 1

Because this is a key technique on which the others are built, you need to stop, practice, and be clear in your mind that you can do it before you add refinements or other complexities. Here is an outline of the technique you just did. Review it carefully, and then continue to practice the technique.

I am going to walk you through it one more time, then try it on your own. Start this way:

1. Choose a pattern. If you can't think of one use "If I'm not perfect, I'm nothing at all," and repeat that six times. Then take the first part and make as your activating phrase "I'm not perfect."

2. Sit in a chair in the neutral position, and begin to slowly, sincerely repeat 10 to 20 times, "I'm not perfect." If you let it happen, and if this is an issue for you, you will feel uncomfortable. Go with it until you sense which direction the emotion is going. You could become sad at first, feeling

how sad you are at recognizing this imperfection, how that is a terrible tragedy for you. Alternately, you could get angry, as the first unconscious associations bring you in touch with the people who put pressure on you, and suddenly you sense your resentment at being put in that position. Remember to say periodically "I'm releasing this negative emotion from the false idea of being perfect."

3. After the feelings are in progress for a while, different possibilities for the second part of the phrase might appear, such as "I'm not perfect . . . It's so terrible . . . I feel so nothing or . . . I'm such a failure." Then go with one of those phrases for a while (there is no particular order). You could then either find another sad phrase or move from sadness to anger—whatever seems right. Trust yourself. You'll know. Suppose it does turn to anger, and these phrases appear: "Why did they do it? . . . They're terrible. . . . I hate them for it." Some of these statements are not patterns but are actually bringing up memories. Allow these memories to appear spontaneously and guide you to the next important phrase to work with. You may have to play with it a little. At first you're going to be inhibited because it may seem like an odd thing to do, but it will be helpful.

4. Take one of the phrases through to completion. After that, take a break. Work effectively with at least one pattern before going further in the reading to help you remember the steps.

ACTIVATION SEQUENCE FOR RELEASING FALSE BELIEFS

1. Start with the desired pattern.
   EXAMPLE: "I'm never good enough for anyone."

2. Tell the truth; repeat the pattern with sincerity.
3. Repeat "I'm never good enough for anyone" 6 times out loud.
4. Repeat "I'm never good enough" 6 to 10 more times.
5. Allow feelings to develop; tears, coughing, or sweating may appear.
6. State "I acknowledge this foolish pattern of 'I'm never good enough for anyone' and am releasing it now."
7. Repeat the releasing phrase 6 to 10 times. Allow additional feelings to surface.
8. Rest for a couple of minutes.
9. Either repeat the same pattern or use one of the new feelings that came up and work with it as an entirely new pattern. The process must then be repeated until the feelings seem to have completely dissipated.

TECHNIQUE 2: Using The Breath To Clear

One way to speed up the releasing process is to use the power of the breath. After activating feelings elicited by your false belief phrase a few times, you will begin to feel uncomfortable in some areas of your body.

Suppose that you have butterflies in your stomach. Instead of exhaling in your usual way, use the "straw" exhale that was described in Chapter 5 and imagine that you are blowing this queasy feeling out of your gut. Continue to repeat the phrases as you are breathing out. The controlled exhalation releases the pattern faster through your conscious intention to clear the gut or solar plexus of butterflies.

You will also notice that the harder you blow and the more that you intend it, the faster the area will clear. Techniques like this work because your mind and body are connected and work together to do as you intend. As you begin to see the benefits of practicing these techniques, you will come to accept how your mind can accomplish this feat.

TECHNIQUE 3: Clearing With Light

Using the color imagery exercise in Chapter 7, see a white light coming out on the exhale as you work to release false belief patterns. The addition of light will further enhance your ability to clear the feeling more quickly, leading the emotion to run dry even faster.

As you visualize the light, the exhalation may first appear dark and grayish. Then, as you see and breathe, it clears and becomes white again. The light acts as a cleansing agent, much as water does.

Stretching and Exaggeration

In releasing, it may also be necessary to open your mouth very wide, stretching your jaw and neck muscles in the process. This may induce gagging, but that response is good and will help you discharge even more quickly. Yoga is an example of a well-known discipline that relies on the power and value of stretching. Stretch your muscles, and you will stretch your ideas as well. Yet even those who practice Yoga could gain a great deal by learning to find tight and blocked places and learning to use the phrases with the intention of releasing troubling false belief patterns.

It is not necessary to be an athlete to release hidden emotion, for your intention is more than half of the process of opening up, and your desire to be open will probably be as important as anything.

When you experience feelings of physical discomfort, don't try to repress or avoid that response, but exaggerate it. Stick your tongue out as far as it will go, and breathe more intensely. The more you are able to exaggerate the feeling, the more you are helping to let it go. The feeling will shudder through you for a few moments, but soon it will be followed by an intense sense of relief. The relief brings with it a pleasurable feeling that will make the discomfort worthwhile.

QUANTIFYING EMOTIONAL RELEASE

It is often difficult to quantify how much emotional energy remains in any one pattern or block. There are no "units of emotion," and getting a clear sense of how much anger one has toward one's father, for example, can be difficult. The unconscious mind, however, comes to the rescue, and, by use of simple images, can give some quantitative feedback that is useful. In theory, one starts with 100% of the emotion and releases down to 0%. This can be expressed visually by using three methods: "open the door," "over the top," and "seeing numbers."

Open the Door

Visualize an ordinary household door that is closed. Agree within yourself that when the door is completely closed, it represents the full content of emotion in a block. Intend that when the door is completely open, no meaningful amount of emotion is left. When visualizing, say to yourself, "Mind, I want you to show me how much emotion is left that I need to release regarding the pattern of my anger with my father for abandoning us (or some pattern that is pertinent in your life)."

The door should open part way. Does it appear to be 20% open? Eighty percent open? The answer should give you a reasonably good idea how much work is left to be done.

Over the Top

A second image that has been found easy to use and reliable utilizes the picture of the parallel lines. Begin by seeing the lines as shoulder-width apart, and imagine them to be your height. In the middle of the lines, at the bottom by your feet, place a big red ball that fits between the lines. The ball is free to travel all the way up to the top of your head and over a bit.

Agree within yourself that when the ball remains at the bottom 100% of the emotion is left. When you ask the mind to show you how much emotion is left regarding pattern X, it will move the ball up your body. When it is free of unnecessary negative emotion, it will go over the top of your head.

Direct Percentage

The third method of trying to quantify the emotional content of your pattern works very well for many people. Simply say to your mind, "On the count of three, show me what percentage of emotion (about one of your patterns) that remains." You should see a specific number.

You can also try all three methods and see if the results from each one match. If they do, you should feel confident that your information is accurate. Check yourself periodically. As you see things change, you will have some confidence that you are making progress even if your illness or other problems are not changing immediately.

The techniques I have described are relatively easy to learn, but learning to release stored feelings is a skill that only develops over time. Be patient if they don't come out as easily as described. The more you work with these feelings, the easier the techniques will become, and the more value they will bring. Once you learn the system and see its value, you will never again let emotion build up, and you will keep yourself clean, just as you shower daily and brush your teeth. Some might call this emotional cleansing the essence of stress management, and that is partly true. But it is more than that—it is growth-oriented rather than simply maintenance- or management-oriented.

CHAPTER 12

INNER COMMUNICATION

By the time you reach this chapter, you should have learned much about how to access your patterns and use imagery and feelings to get at the truth. There is another way to get information from yourself—"talk to your mind." I will now show you how to explore your inner mind and how you can best communicate with it.

Although you are one person with one personality, it often seems as if there are at least two of you—deeply conflicted or undecided on which action to take on a given issue. You may say something like, "My mind says yes, but my heart says no," or "My gut feeling is to do it, but my heart or mind says no." This division within yourself, the conflicting opinions, is what gives rise to doubt.

The choices you make become what you ultimately communicate to the outside world. Sometimes you may be aware of being dissatisfied with your final choice. You may be unaware, however, of any remaining indecision or incompleteness. Your indecision could reveal itself as passive-aggressive behavior: a headache, a cold, or unexplained sadness. Your final decision, often the result of long and difficult inner communication, becomes your outer communication.

Decisions become all the more difficult when you don't know your own mind. In this chapter you will identify more specifically the parts of yourself involved in these inner decisions and communications, so that you can access and communicate more openly and freely within yourself.

This chapter will help you to:

1. know what you really want,
2. know what blocks or resistances lie within you, and
3. further understand the nature of who you really are.

WHO'S INSIDE, ANYWAY?

Suppose that you're trying to decide what kind of food you want for dinner. You've narrowed your choices to Chinese and Japanese. Inside your head you might think (hear) something like this:

SIDE 1	SIDE 2
I have a real taste for some good Chinese food tonight.	Yeah, but Japanese food is better for me. It's lower in calories and fat.
But I love Chinese egg rolls and dumplings.	But Japanese is easier to digest, better for my diet. . . .
But . . . etc.	But . . . etc.

In the end, you choose Chinese. You're having a discussion, but who are you talking to? To discover this, you must analyze the self-talk in detail.

First, no matter what the outcome may be in this example, no great loss or gain is likely to occur. The lack of real importance means that very few deep or unconscious issues are likely to surface, and the probability of feeling you've made the wrong choice is small. This is significant because the more important a decision is, the deeper and more complicated the inner thought processes are likely to be, and the greater the long-term impact might be.

Although the two sides appear to be opposite, they are actually complementary parts of the "self" that you know. Arguments on either side are familiar and can be said to represent the "real" you. Your two sides are rationally reviewing the pros and cons of each cuisine, a familiar sort of choice with which most people can easily identify. You chose Chinese food because your desire won over the rational-mental self, which argued for the health benefits of Japanese food.

Now, let's assume you got stuck in this dialogue and couldn't decide the issue. In all likelihood, a third side might have emerged, possibly experienced as a funny feeling in your gut. This feeling might be verbalized as, "I've got a gut feeling that Chinese food is right." You can't explain why, but despite the fact that there is no particular basis for the feeling, it seems right. And it's strong enough to override either the heart or the mind, depending on the situation.

In some people, this mid-abdominal sensation of "It feels right" is often heavily involved in decision making, whereas in others, gut feelings are rare. Usually gut feelings come into play in more emotionally charged situations than picking out a restaurant. They can be reliably used to make such choices as what horse to bet on, what stock to invest in, or even whom to choose as a spouse. This vague bodily sensation, which can be quite convincing, is the physical evidence of a deeper you—the you that lies within.

THE UNCONSCIOUS

I will use the word *unconscious* to refer to that part of the self that seems hidden or unseen from the conscious you. (You may think of this as the subconscious.) The unconscious is a huge part of the self and has several functions and abilities that operate automatically day or night, whether you want it to or not. The unconscious does the following:

1. Makes a permanent record of all your known experiences from sometime prior to your birth, including actual events, misperceptions, and feelings.
2. Makes assessments, conclusions, and decisions based on life experiences, which are then used to make further decisions and choices.
3. Operates as the middleman between your conscious bodily perceptions and the body itself.
4. Is the repository of your belief system and the source from which virtually all thoughts, words, and behaviors are derived.
5. Follows through on decisions made by breaking into consciousness and calling attention to them.

One unique part of the unconscious mind is called the conscience. The conscience is supposed to be the part of your unconscious that knows right from wrong. It's the part that can break through with a thought or a feeling that says, "You'd better not do that," "It's wrong," or "You'll be sorry." The conscience can be useful if the behavior being monitored is being propelled in the direction of your belief system programming. In that sense, the conscience is just "doing its job."

Conflicts often arise from the confusing or opposite beliefs you hold on a subject. Conflict is also generated between the relatively uninformed conscious mind and the knowledgeable, often behavior-driven, unconscious mind. For example, a person who consciously pursues a career in sales with the expectation that he will succeed may unconsciously believe he's not convincing or worthy of success. He may remain unaware indefinitely, unless he takes the time and the effort to find out why he is unsuccessful.

When people sincerely say that they're going to do something, yet never seem to do it, it is generally because of a conflict between a conscious desire and the hidden true belief or desire. We cannot truly know our own minds until we probe deep within our unconscious to find out why we do what we do.

The unconscious, then, operates relatively silently in a general goal-directed fashion. However, if the beliefs are opposite to the goal, no progress can be made. The unconscious will do its best to carry out what seems to be the right thing to do, even if it means making you miserable, as in the case of the addicted person. Alcoholics and drug addicts are often consciously aware that their behavior is foolish and self-destructive, but their underlying fear and their belief programs are so strong that they find themselves unable to stop. From the point of view of the unconscious, it is less miserable to lie drunk in the gutter than to face the misery of real life.

You can also make yourself miserable if you ignore a thought or action deemed to be important by the unconscious. The result can be pain, sadness, a nightmare, or other inner disturbance. Because the unconscious mind is much more astute at understanding what's going on around it and determining appropriate action than is the conscious self, it becomes all the more important to know the true unconscious mind.

THE THREE SIDES

In the dialogue about what food to eat for dinner, there are three "sides." First is the mental part, representing reason and logic; second is the emotional part, representing desire; and third is the gut level, representing intuitive feeling. Intuition, or gut feeling, is a shortcut to a conscious decision because it brings into consciousness something from underneath, something that was not consciously remembered or thought about, such as the inner beliefs that support the ideas expressed consciously.

For example, any or all of the following beliefs could have played a role in the conscious decision to eat Chinese food.

1. To be healthy you need discipline.
2. Health is all mental anyway.
3. Nothing kills you faster than worry.
4. I deserve to eat what I want.

These beliefs generate additional beliefs, which form the basis for the choices made.

5. One meal isn't worth worrying about.
6. Eating is one of the few pleasures I have left.

When your beliefs appear to conflict, as with items 1 versus 4 or 5, the unconscious mind can throw in a supporting memory, such as "Uncle Joe ate and drank whatever he liked, and he lived to be 95." This justifies the belief and helps to make the choice.

Many people are not aware that these thoughts are percolating beneath the surface. The thoughts need to be looked for consciously, which we will explore in the exercises to come. Although this may seem like a lot of thinking for an egg roll, it's not so much when it comes to something as important as your career, marriage, or health. You will soon discover for yourself how truly complex human beings are.

You must come to know this analyzing, assessing unconscious mind, and you must learn to challenge its beliefs, assessments, conclusions, and decisions. You must learn to challenge your own thoughts when there is a repeating pattern of pain or unhappiness. When you make a decision or come to a conclusion that is unhealthy or unwise from a conscious viewpoint, you must make a conscious effort to ask that part of yourself, "How did I come to that idea?" You must learn a different way of interacting with yourself.

The model for inner communication may be unlike anything you have seen or heard before. In fact, I'd be surprised if you had, considering how few people know how to communicate with their unconscious.

CONTACTING THE OTHER YOU

In order to gain an understanding of our unconscious thought processes, let's follow the thinking of Joe, a salesman who worked for a man named Fred before being laid off by the company. Although Joe's termination wasn't Fred's fault, Joe blames him. The following dialogue transpired at a chance meeting in a Chinese restaurant.

Fred: Joe, how good to see you. I was going to call you soon. Please join me at my table.

Joe: No thanks. I'd rather not.

Fred: C'mon. There's something important I'd like to talk to you about.

Joe: Alright, if you insist.

Fred: You don't know this, but I've joined a new organization, and I'd like you on my team. You're a good salesman, Joe.

Joe: Really? Then how come you terminated me before?

Fred: I didn't. The company did over my objections. This opportunity has great potential.

Joe: I don't know, Fred. I really don't.

Fred: Think about it. I'll call you in a few days.

Joe: Sure. Thanks.

In light of his previous experience with Fred, Joe might wonder if he can be trusted. Deciding whether or not to accept a job opportunity—especially from someone you're not sure you can trust—takes some thought. Joe needs to find out what he thinks and feels deep down inside. He knows he can't simply dismiss Fred without going deeply into the pros and cons of the job offer and his gut response to Fred. Joe asks his unconscious mind for any information he might be able to use to make his decision—he goes straight to the horse's mouth, so to speak. He approaches his unconscious mind, which has been watching somewhat objectively.

Dialogue Between the Conscious and Unconscious Mind

In the following interchange, CJ is Conscious Joe and UJ is Unconscious Joe.

CJ: Why do you feel so uncomfortable with Fred's proposal?

UJ: (Silence.)

CJ: Tell me. Is it because of what happened last time, or is there something more?

UJ: Something more.

CJ: I'm not aware of it. Tell me about it.

UJ: Are you sure you want to know?

CJ: Of course I'm sure.

UJ: You're afraid of failing.

CJ: I'm afraid of failing? Why do you say that?

UJ: Because.

CJ: Of what?

UJ: You're afraid you might fail at a real opportunity, and you would have no excuses left.

CJ: I want success very badly. Why do I need excuses?

UJ: You don't believe you deserve it.

CJ: I doubt that what you're saying is true, but suppose for a moment that it is. *Why* am I afraid of success?

UJ: You're not as good as the others—you're not really worthy.

Notice that this dialogue takes a different approach to gaining information compared with the method used in the restaurant dialogue. Joe is engaged in a dialogue as if he were talking to another person rather than the other half of his mind. If Joe were to decide on his job by dialoguing in a fashion similar to the restaurant dialogue, it might go like this:

Three Sides of Joe

Joe A: I wonder if I should take this job. It might have potential.

Joe B: Maybe, but Fred screwed me before.

Joe A: Yeah, but maybe he's trying to make up for it.

Joe B: So what. He feels guilty, and he's going to throw me a bone.

Joe A: But people change. I could use a break.

Joe C: Naw, I don't feel right about it. I have a gut feeling it's nothing—a dead-end deal.

Joe seems undecided until he gets a gut feeling that it's a bad deal. He trusts his feelings—usually a good idea if the underlying beliefs are correct. But are they? What are Joe's beliefs?

Recall from Joe's conversation with his unconscious mind that he believes he's determined to fail, that he is unworthy of success, and that he is not as good as others. These ideas are working unconsciously to undermine his chances for success and are leading to poor life choices. He needs to become aware of these unconscious beliefs—to test them to see if they are correct—before acting upon them.

One way to verify his beliefs is to ask, deep down inside, "Do I feel unworthy of success?" As he asks the question, Joe might feel his chest tighten, or his breathing might change. Or he could test the truth of his beliefs through dialogue with an image. For example, he could say, "In front of me is a door. I'm going to intend that if the door opens, I'm totally worthy to succeed; if I'm unworthy, the door will remain closed." The answer is the same; the unconscious mind is consistent. Part of Joe actually believes that he's worthless and destined to fail. Although he may feel unsure of himself at times, on a conscious level, Joe probably believes he would be a success if he ever got the right opportunity.

In order to make a successful choice, Joe needs to believe that his conscious mind is different from his unconscious mind, and he needs to know the truth about his beliefs. The best way to get the truth is simply to ask, as Joe does in the dialogue above. Notice the way he talks. First, he's honest. He admits ignorance and is open and available to information. Second, he is somewhat doubtful, but states clearly that he's open to being convinced. Third, he is persistent. The unconscious mind can be very temperamental and often needs coaxing.

The need for objectivity in seeing, hearing, and feeling your thoughts and beliefs has frequently been stressed. In order to analyze and later correct false ideas, you must know what's real and what's not. No matter how convinced he is of his unworthiness, Joe must approach this belief as something that must be eliminated because it interferes with his access to prosperity. The belief was acquired through misunderstanding, parenting, and/or experience, and the process of releasing that belief through dialoguing begins with the acknowledgment of what is and then a statement of what will be. Again, CJ is Conscious Joe and UJ is Unconscious Joe.

CJ: So, I don't believe I deserve success.

UJ: Yes.

CJ: I know that is a completely illogical and foolish belief, and I begin to release it now.

UJ: (Silence.)

CJ: I no longer choose to believe in you. You are released. I no longer need you.

UJ: I can't release it. I'm afraid.

CJ: Of what?

UJ: I don't know. I'm afraid it just won't work out somehow.

CJ: It can work out, and it will.

We see, then, that the unconscious is fearful and uncertain of change. Merely thinking positive will not be enough to dislodge the belief—both the belief and the unconscious mind will resist with great effort.

False beliefs remain in place partly because of fear about what will happen if they are released. Dialoguing pinpoints the mental or verbal aspect of the false belief, but the more unyielding and tenacious aspect of fear—the true feeling portion—must often be released through different processes. Some of these have been covered in earlier chapters.

Like Joe, you have an inner voice that talks to you. This type of inner dialogue is readily available to you *now*, without psychoanalysis, hypnosis, deep relaxation, or other special techniques. But you must question, you must approach it as you would a friend or confidante. And you must challenge it and demand to know your inner truth. Finally, you must believe in your ability to make successful choices. If you don't believe in something deep down inside, it's not going to happen.

Don't forget that these fearful statements arising from the unconscious are a small fraction of the unconscious mind. The negative part seems predominant only because it is being focused on and is the conflicted area for study. In no way does it represent the vast resources of the mind, which is primarily positive in tone.

THE EVIL ONE

Not long ago, a young woman came to me because she was struggling to figure out why her life wasn't going anywhere, despite her best efforts, good looks, charming personality, discipline, and enthusiasm. She stated that she was always working for peanuts and making money for others without any appreciation. She had also been through a number of marginally fulfilling relationships and felt something was wrong somewhere. She was more irritated and confused than she was depressed.

After obtaining the basic history, I began to teach her the techniques to contact her inner self, which she learned quickly. The following is the beginning of her inner dialogue. C is her conscious self and U her unconscious self:

C: Why don't I have any money?

U: You don't have any money because if you did, you wouldn't need a man for anything but sex.

She repeated out loud what she had heard her unconscious say, then asked me, "Where is this coming from? Me?"

"Of course," I answered. "Who else?"

"But it was just there—like that!" she said, snapping her fingers.

"You were ready," I replied.

The young woman reflected for a moment. "I hadn't really thought about it, but if I were rich, I wouldn't need a man like I do now." Astonished at what she had discovered, she thought about it some more before she continued:

C: Is there another reason?

U: Yes.

C: What is it?

U: You don't deserve it.

C: Why?

U: Because you're evil.

C: Evil? How so?

U: Because you hurt your father by being born accidentally. He didn't want you.

C: Why not?

U: Because he had to marry your mother and become responsible. It's all your fault. You don't deserve success.

Again, she didn't know how she came to this belief, but I presented a couple of possibilities. First, she came to this conclusion by misinterpreting things she may have seen or heard. Or she may have overheard such a statement as a child and had forgotten about it, storing it in her unconscious mind for later use in drawing conclusions.

Early in her childhood, the woman had been taught that talking to her "self" in this way was like talking to the devil, so initially she was fearful and reluctant to do so. However, once she recognized that it was simply a part of herself and that there was nothing to fear and everything to gain, she began to dialogue intensively. Her intention was to discover and work on every part of her hidden self. Having discovered a previously unknown pattern that guaranteed her failure in relationships and financial matters, she began to demand more and more answers and reasons for all that had befallen her. She proceeded to work out many of her issues regarding men, independence, and financial prosperity. By using this technique, she was able to make a breakthrough in a short time, greatly speeding her progress and success.

Sometimes, although you are willing to change your false beliefs, doing so is not easy. You may have to ask more than once to get to the truth.

THE RELUCTANT UNCONSCIOUS

Sometimes it's hard to make the desired change in your unconscious mind. In fact, the unconscious is reluctant to give up any information to the conscious mind or change its ways without some real effort. In one group with whom I worked, for example, the participants commented, "It's not talking. I can't hear anything." They were asking, "What function does cancer serve in my life?" With very deep and possibly painful questions, the unconscious mind wants to be absolutely certain that you really want an answer.

One of the most common difficulties that people have in developing their own awareness is their reluctance to know the truth. They are fearful of discovering their deepest fears and admitting them when they are revealed. They'd rather not confront a core fear of abandonment or deeply held feelings of worthlessness. The unconscious is duty-bound to "protect" them from pain that, deep down inside, they don't want. Therefore, you must be prepared to be insistent and demanding in order to convince your inner mind of your willingness to experience some discomfort or disbelief.

Though initially unresponsive, the unconscious mind can be reached by asking progressively more assertive questions until an answer is received. In the following example, "X" could relate to anything in your life (for example, cancer, low self-esteem, or a failed marriage):

C: I'd like to know the reason for X.

U: (Silence.)

C: I repeat. I want to know the reason for X.

U: (More silence.)

C: I demand to know the reason for X.

U: (Continued silence.)

C: Without fear, hesitation, or doubt, no matter what the truth is, I must have it.

U: (Silence.)

C: I am not leaving this chair, nor will I open my eyes, until I have an answer. I repeat: What purpose does X serve me now?

U: I don't know.

C: That's no answer. Think again.

U: (No response.)

C: Look, my friend, we're all on the same team. You want me to get better. I want me to get better. So why don't you just tell me what I need to know?

U: I'm afraid to be alone.

The response at this point still may be fragmentary, but headway has been made, and with this opening more and more information will be released. Start with easier questions to get the mind going, rather than expect the absolute deepest fears and beliefs to be revealed immediately. Give yourself a chance. This is a new concept for you. Remember, your unconscious mind is not going to give you any information until it believes that you are entirely serious about wanting to receive it.

Recall that in the psychofeedback exercises in Chapter 9, you made certain statements to your unconscious in order to allow it to give you the information that you requested. The greatest mistake people make when attempting an inner dialogue is giving up too easily. Don't quit after asking once or twice. In the past, hypnosis has been used successfully in revealing hidden information, but if you have done any of the exercises in this book, you should find it possible to access your mind simply by using assertive and positive approaches.

Sometimes you can tap into a very negative core, and it may be scary if you don't handle it properly. For example:

C: Am I going to beat this cancer?

U: You'll never fight this cancer and win.

C: Oh, really? Who says?

U: I do.

C: Oh, really? Who are you?

U: I'm you.

C: No, you're not. You're a fearful little child who's afraid of his own shadow.

U: (Pause.) It's too tough, and it's too late.

C: Why do you say that?

U: I know you. You're lazy. You haven't got what it takes.

C: Maybe, maybe not. Maybe there was never anything important enough to fight for before.

U: I know you. You're a quitter.

C: You only think you know me. I'm a fighter now.

U: What will you do?

C: For one thing, we're finally talking, so instead of hurting me and depressing me, why not help me? Give me some encouragement and hope.

U: I don't know if I can.

C: I don't know that you can't.

U: Well, maybe I can.

C: Thank you. I appreciate you. We are one, you know.

In this dialogue, part of the unconscious is doubtful and seems more negative and less objective than before. This, of course, doesn't represent the whole unconscious, but it is a valid part and must be acknowledged and worked with if you are to progress. Notice that the conscious self doesn't attempt to deny the feelings outright, but has a "perhaps," or "yes, but" attitude, thereby engendering less resistance than denial of a believed truth. Every part of you is valid—even the fearful, childish, doubtful parts—and each part must be treated with respect.

The more distance you can put between the fearful, negative self and your conscious self, the better the inner dialogue will work. Frequently in my private sessions, I feed the dialogue to the conscious part, while the person reports back what the unconscious says in response. With a little practice and coaching, you will quickly learn how to get the most out of yourself. I recommend that you address that other part as "you" instead of "I." Rather than saying, for example, "Why am I so fearful?" say, "Why do *you* make me fearful? Why do *you* think I can't beat my cancer? Who are *you*, and what do *you* want from me?" Remember, the conscious you is, by nature and definition, self-loving, positive, and confident. Only the unconscious you carries the doubts, fears, and worries.

A standard, and very important, question to ask whenever you're involved in inner dialogue in this fashion is "What is it that you fear?" because, in fact, most things break down to some kind of fear. The more precise you are and the more serious that it (you) believes you are, the more likely you are to receive the information you desire.

Let's not forget that good inner communication always leads to good outer communication, as well. When you know the reasons behind what you say and do, you can't help but change your life in a positive way.

SUMMING UP

I have presented a number of different ideas on inner communications. In brief, these can be summarized as follows:

1. Outer communication comes from inner communication.
2. There are at least two separate parts to you: a vast unconscious self and a conscious self.
3. The unconscious, after collecting all the data, makes assessments, conclusions, and decisions based on your life experience. These are used to make further decisions and choices.
4. The conscience may be thought of as a small part of the unconscious.
5. The unconscious will break through into conscious awareness in order to give you a message. The message can take the form of words, moods, or physical feelings.
6. Psychofeedback may be used to corroborate your inner dialogue.
7. The unconscious is reluctant to give up its information. It must be cajoled, challenged, and reassured of your sincerity.
8. Negative messages are accepted matter-of-factly and responded to with clear, positive, active statements. Keep your distance. Remember, it's not the real you.

9. Never accept a "no," "I don't know" or a silent answer from the unconscious. Always remember to persevere. Never stop trying until you get the answers that you desire.

10. Inner communication leads to good outer communication and is a key to successful relationships.

EXERCISES IN INNER COMMUNICATION

Now that you have learned the basic theory of inner communication, it's time to practice some inner dialogue so that you can meet and beat resistance. You will begin by writing some of the questions that you would like to have answered. They can be drawn from your images, your psychofeedback inquiries, or simple thoughts. The following are a few suggestions to help you get started.

Exercise 1

1. What do I get from the relationship with X now?
2. Why do I allow myself to be hurt by X?
3. What do I really desire from X?
4. What is the value of my cancer to me?
5. What is my greatest stumbling block to fighting my alcoholism with all my might?
6. Why don't I engage in those practices that are most helpful to me?

Begin by closing your eyes and getting into a relaxed, neutral position. (It is not necessary to be deeply relaxed.) Take a few deep breaths. Then begin, in a straightforward manner, to ask the questions that you desire to be answered. Remember, ask the questions as if you were dialoguing with someone else.

When you don't get an answer immediately, get assertive, as if you were speaking to someone difficult. Decide that you will not leave the chair or open your eyes until you get some answers.

Exercise 2

Now replay the negative messages you've been hearing—the "can'ts," the "won'ts," the doubts. Take each sentence individually and work on it. It could get complicated, so take notes. Now challenge the reason for those beliefs. Accept what is said, and then argue with that unconscious part of yourself as "you," not "I." When you get a response that says you are weak, stupid, unworthy, or any other negative statement, ask:

1. Where did you get that idea?
2. Who told you?
3. Why did you accept that conclusion in the first place?
4. What's the point of continually feeding me self-defeating messages?
5. What do you really want from me?
6. I'm not afraid of you. Show yourself to me in an image, so that I can see you better.

Remember, in the process of challenge, never deny or ignore a statement. Rather, say something like "I hear you," "I see your point," or "It's an interesting idea." Then retort with, "But the truth is X." Keep the lines of communication open and begin to truly know yourself.

CHAPTER 13

VISUALIZATION AND PATTERN RELEASE

Up to this point we have relied on repetition of words, breathing, and visualization with the white light as a means to achieve pattern release. Visualization is an extremely powerful tool for dealing with one's problems. Often you have heard that you must face your problems, open your eyes to them. What is really meant is see your problems clearly if you wish to solve them.

In this chapter we will use visualization to aid in pattern release. There are a number of different ways to use pictures to do this, and by the time we are done, you'll have some techniques of your own.

In the psychofeedback chapter (Chapter 9), we used the crossed and parallel lines as a way to help find patterns. This method can also be used to detect a blocked pattern. A block is defined as the point or focus in mind or body that prevents the optimal flow of energies. These terms are used liberally to mean a specific problem caused by a group of patterns and the place on the body where one experiences soreness or discomfort.

One pattern doesn't make a block, for there are usually many intertwined beliefs, all wound around and crossing over one another. However, we can work symbolically and use the X to represent any false belief pattern. Now we work with the X much as we did with the psychofeedback technique, by first visualizing it, then thinking or saying things, and seeing whether the X remains or changes to the alternate position (parallel lines). This parallel, open position represents free flowing energy, indicating that harmful negative emotional energy is being released. The major difference is the way in which you will visualize the X in the following exercises to release the pattern (block).

Pick any pattern you wish, and represent that pattern with an X in your mind. Then, *without using word repetition,* use any means to release the pattern and get the X to open. It may help to visualize yourself moving the arms of the X with your hands. You may demand, cajole, will it, or open it any way you like.

Did you succeed in opening one of your patterns this way? Probably not, because the pattern hasn't been activated. This means that it's too deeply entrenched to be released by willpower or desire alone. It is as real as a loud noise that you may try to ignore or sunburned skin, but in the end they are still there. It is important that you understand what the X represents. People sometimes mistakenly believe that because the X is only a figment of their imaginations, they can make it go away at will. They cannot, however, because they have tied the image to a real entity, a false belief pattern, and now it is no longer imaginary. To release a pattern, you must bring it up from where it is hidden and activate it by repeating it as you did in the techniques described in Chapter 11.

Try very hard now to feel any resistance to opening the X. If you take my suggestion and visualize it in front of you and try to pull it apart with your hands, it will resist like iron (see Figure 12 on page 175). The resistance is equal to the strength and

PULLING APART THE "X"

Figure 12

depth of feelings in the pattern. The resistance is what you are trying to overcome, and knowing how much there is gives you a rough estimate of how much work or repetition might be required to ultimately release it.

RELEASING WITH THE X TECHNIQUE

Begin with any pattern. (For example, "If I'm not perfect, I'm nothing at all.") See the X in your mind, and declare that it now represents the whole pattern that you are working on. Then repeat the pattern 5 or 6 times. Continue with "I'm not perfect" 6 to 8 times as before, continuing through to the releasing section.

Your intention is to repeat the cycle of acknowledging and releasing until the X begins to open. You are using the X as a marker to follow as you do the activation to release sequence. As emotion is released, the position of the lines uncrosses to form parallel lines. As you begin to make some headway, you will notice the lines moving, and you'll get feedback about how you are doing.

Fighting Resistance Through Inner Dialogue

You are now able to add even more versatility and power to your releasing by using inner dialogue with the X as a way to work with the resistance. *Expect resistance.* The process of change means there will be some inner conflicts—parts of you will be trying to get free while other parts will be afraid of facing things and of change.

If not much seems to be happening as you repeat the patterns, ask the X why it resists releasing the pattern. The information may come back as inner dialogue, a picture, or even additional feelings. If you have captured the essence of the pattern with the X, it will respond to your demands to know what blocks are in the way of releasing the pattern at hand. When you have found a part of yourself that resists change, you must find out why it is struggling against the common good.

Usually when one part of you struggles against change, that part fears either additional pain or that a need will not be met. There are some techniques that use the concept of an "inner child." The inner child represents an unmet need. It is useful to try to embrace the image of the child-self to give it comfort and help it—you—feel better. It needs comfort because it has pain, and it will resist change until that pain is acknowledged and comfort is given. The opening of the X is a way of sensing if that need is met and healing is taking place. (If you are not familiar with the concept of the inner child, see "Suggested Reading" at the end of this book.)

Body Position and the Flow

In order to facilitate the X coming open, your body must be open as well. Rest your arms at your sides so they're not touching at all. (See Figure 13.) This will indicate to your mind that you are ready for the release and have no desire or need to resist. Your legs must not be crossed; rather, spread them apart with your feet propped up on something or flat on the floor. This reflects your total trust and willingness to let the energies flow through.

Now intend that the energy move *from the top of your body through your neck, chest, abdomen, pelvis, and down through both legs and out your feet.* You're directing the released emotional energy to flow through your feet into the ground. Let Mother Nature take care of the excess energy. The secret to gaining con-

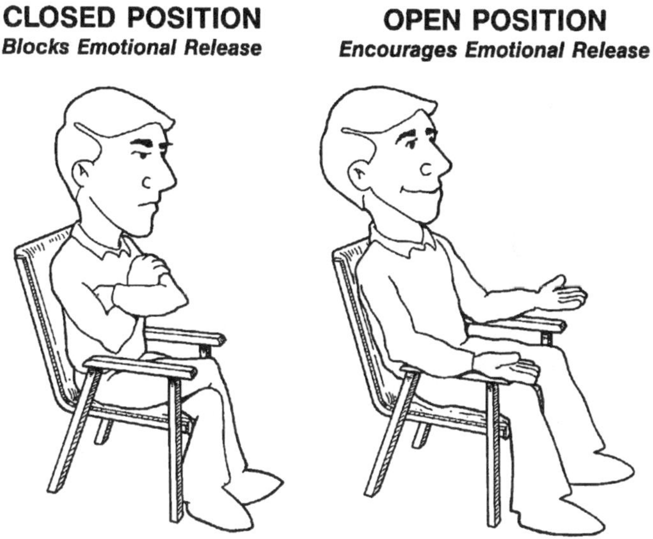

Figure 13

trol of your feelings is to allow them to flow through your body. Every time you feel yourself tighten up or pull inward, as if to restrict the flow, take a breath. Bring your attention directly into the feelings, and think only of letting them move downward. As you do this, the X should be gradually opening. (See Figure 13.)

As you learned in the psychofeedback chapter (Chapter 9), notice where any pain occurs, such as around the navel or in the shoulder or chest. Wherever the feelings are, try to move them into the center of your body, then into the pelvis and down each leg into the floor. Sometimes just going through the pelvic area is enough to clear it.

You may also move something that is on one side or other down that side and out of the body. For example, pain over the liver on the right can be sent down the right leg. As you gain skill with this maneuver, you will never again be afraid to release your feelings because they might be too powerful or painful. The activation leading to acknowledgment and release gets the energies moving, but the real task is done when you can be certain they moved out of the bottoms of your feet.

When you hear of someone being grounded as opposed to flighty or spacey, it means the person naturally moves his or her emotional energy into the ground. As a result, grounded people feel connected, secure, and solid in themselves, which is how you want to be.

As you experience the flow of negative patterns, you will have a sense of the ease or difficulty of the process. This is giving you instantaneous feedback on how you're doing. The wider the lines of the X open, the more you have cleared. You can even visualize yourself going between the parallel lines, meaning that you are going deeper and deeper into the pattern.

When you set your body to do the releasing, you will notice that at first it will involuntarily move inward to protect the pelvis, or your arms will move inward to protect your heart. Even movements in your little finger are important and symbolize some resistance.

Continue to clear the pattern, going through the complete cycle of acknowledging and releasing for 4 to 10 minutes.

Variations on a Theme

Nan had been troubled by chronic muscle aches, tightening of the skin, and decreased range of motion in the affected limbs. She also was very fatigued most of the time and spent a lot of time resting and recovering while taking all kinds of medications. She was considered to have a rare variant of an otherwise rare disease.

She was highly motivated and we used the X in a special way. We would think of patterns that we felt were important in her life and placed the X over the affected muscle areas. As she released the anger toward her father and sister the X would open up right over the target area and the pain would be relieved. Little by little the majority of the pain was relieved. Seeing it change in that way was a strong reinforcer of the power of emotion.

An excellent way to help relieve a pain or help with any chronic dysfunction is to put the patterns over a physically compromised area and note what happens as various patterns are released. You can always check if they are related first by asking through psychofeedback, "Is this one related to my pain or that one?" You are attempting to remove as many emotion-laden patterns as possible. Moving the X over an area directly involved gives you one more piece of feedback to guide you to the right solution to your problems. It is also one more indication of the flexibility and utility of one simple image.

Putting It All Together

What was left out of our description of Nan's technique was that she didn't merely use the X, but combined all of the previous techniques together. She not only activated, but also breathed and used light as well. Sometimes it hurt physically as well as emotionally, and she would let out a yell, which was very helpful too.

With a little practice, you will be able to use all of these techniques—X, breath, and light—simultaneously. The X gives you a target to work with. The parallel lines can be represented by your arms and legs to target the breath and light, giving you a track or a channel in which to push the negative energy through. You can then flush the energies out of your body right through your pelvis, legs, and feet. After a while you'll be able to see the negative energy as gray or dark which lightens up as you move it through.

Visualizing to Activate

It is possible to begin your pattern release exercise with a visualization—without words, and then find some phrase or belief that you will use to ultimately bring up the feelings. This imagining process is already an integral part of your innate abilities. Many of you have probably used visualization techniques as part of your rehearsal for meeting a new and challenging behavior. Now use the process of visualization to activate and release emotional blocks.

Find an image in which you see yourself participating but resist doing, and then push mentally into this resistance. You will find yourself naturally saying "I can't," or "I'm afraid," or "I won't," and as you repeat these words, feelings will begin to surface. As you continue to push harder into the image, you generate more resistance, and more feelings begin to come up.

Tony complained of a fear of going over bridges. He didn't know how or why it happened, but one day he found that he could not cross a bridge without feeling intense anxiety. He was frightened beyond rational thought and hadn't the vaguest idea why. He found that if he took a few drinks he could do it, but after a few drinks he was in no condition to drive.

To help Tony, we began with the only information we had: When he came to a bridge, he would begin to feel anxious. We started by having him imagine beginning to enter the bridge. I asked him to tell me how he felt, to which he said "I can't. I can't. I can't do it." "I'll die. I'll die. Oh God, I'll die! It will collapse. It's collapsing! I can't take it. I can't take it!"

We constructed a pattern based on the deep feeling that he would die if he crossed the bridge. He worked with that pattern, acknowledging and releasing and letting feelings and thoughts surface. Over a period of weeks, as he forced himself to cross the bridge mentally, various memories and other associations emerged. Several things were collapsing simultaneously in Tony's life. He finally admitted that he would find himself in the middle of the street or unknown locales and not know where he was or how he got there. Frequently, he had a gun in his hand. He was terrified that his stable personality was collapsing.

It took some time before Tony would even approach a bridge, let alone cross one, but he eventually did so without medication or alcohol.

This was an unusual case, and Tony needed a lot of support, but the basic process is the same whatever the problem. Remember these steps:

1. Find the image of the problem and focus intently on it.
2. Tell the truth of how you feel, as you press into the image.
3. Create a sentence and pattern from it.
4. Release the pattern as you have been taught.

Any picture you see that upsets you will stimulate the "I can't" or "I'm afraid" feelings as you press into it. This fear can cover up the deeper feelings that are usually the ones you are trying to access. Sometimes the best you can do is diminish extremely disturbing emotions, if you are not able to allow yourself to visualize the object of your fear or other feelings. Try not to be afraid of your mind, for once you know how it works, it won't be able to frighten you. You must, however, be willing to look at and participate in the image and push yourself in order to make it an effective technique. Going into the resistance is the single best way to make deep feelings surface. You may then add other techniques as suggested.

A Common Situation

One practical way to use this is, for example, in trying to approach your boss for a raise. Let's suppose that you cannot muster the courage to ask, although you feel that you must. One way to get around the fear might be to simply visualize yourself going through the motions and, so the theory goes, by rehearsing this activity, you will find the needed strength and courage to carry it through. It is, however, possible that you will not find that strength and that the fear will still be there. You need to get some of that fear out before you can actually confront the boss, or do the rehearsal technique.

The confrontational visualizations can be used. See yourself as you are about to confront the boss—perhaps some place in the office as you knock on the door, or walking up to the office. You'll begin to experience the fear well up. As you press into the fear, part of you says, "I can't," or "I'm afraid." The "I can't" becomes your activating phrase, and from there you repeat as before, "I can't. I can't. I can't," until the next word comes up. "I can't. I can't. He'll . . . I can't. He'll hurt me. I can't. He'll fire me. . . . I'll be alone. . . . I'll have nothing. I failed." Each of these deeper phrases, separately or together, when repeated, activate deeper feeling states. When repeated over and over without restriction, the phrases allow the fear, anger, or sadness to appear.

If the issue is dealing with more than simply a raise, and some fears or concerns are underneath all of that, then allowing that emotion to be discharged can give you the strength to go forth. Remember that your fears, your false beliefs, are held in place by the emotions themselves. As the emotion is discharged, the fear and the thought of what will happen will begin to change in your mind. Thus, after you discharge the underlying fear or anger, you can go back and do the rehearsal visualization to present your position to the boss. You are then much more likely to deal effectively with him or her. The act of forcing yourself to perform in a visualization in a way that stimulates resistance is an excellent way to find out why you refuse or resist any process.

Discharge of Feelings Leads to New Ideas

The second part of a thought, belief, or pattern is the mental or word portion. I have discussed feelings in detail and described the bimodal nature of thought—that is, thoughts are both emotional and mental and have feelings and words. With the emotions at least somewhat discharged, we can look more closely at the idea contained in the belief.

Suppose you hold the belief that says, "I feel unworthy because nobody loves me." After some of the sad and angry feelings that are associated with that belief have been released, you will be left, perhaps, in a quandary, not knowing what to think or feel. You might think, "I can't really say I feel unworthy at this moment just because no one loves me, because now I feel somewhat different." You might say instead, "I wonder why no one loves me because I don't really think (feel) I'm so bad."

Your feeling state says one thing, whereas your experience leads you to believe another. You are now abandoning your previous experience as a criterion for maintaining your beliefs. You will have decided that the only thing worth believing is what works and what makes life get better. This leaves you free, then, to play with your thoughts (words) in order to reorder them in a way that is consistent with your new feelings.

AFFIRMATIONS AND PATTERNS

As you might imagine, changing your old, negative images and thoughts to positive new ones disrupts what was previously a fairly stable system. This instability works to your advantage by creating a void in your belief structure, as your mind now reorganizes and decides what to think and believe. This void says, in effect, "If that's not the truth, then what is?" It is at this time, when your new belief systems are being laid down, that affirmations are most valuable.

Affirmations are statements of truth that you wish to believe. The classic is: *Each and every day in each and every way, I am getting better and better.* It is an affirmation of a living truth. The statements "I'm strong, healthy, and powerful" or "I can give and receive love easily and unconditionally" are both positive affirmations. There are also negative affirmations, such as "I'm a big dummy and can't do anything right" but you already know too much about those! The principle is the same, however: If you repeat the phrase often enough, you come to believe it, which helps make it true, further reinforcing the belief, and so the cycle goes.

You want to affirm the positive and do it most efficiently. The most efficient way is when the belief structure is open, vulnerable, and undergoing change. The affirmations can be added directly onto the pattern as it is being removed. For example, "I release the silly notion that I am worthless without love, and I affirm that I am perfect just the way I am and I'm able to give and receive love."

Those are two separate affirmations. For every statement of release, you counter with "I am strong, brave, proud, worthy, decent, loving, etc." In some way that is a clear affirmation of the truth. Remember, repetition promotes learning. The more you say it convincingly, the more you will believe it. Your parents or others programmed you to believe you were worthless or a failure or somehow inadequate, and you are now countering that programming.

The problem with affirming without breaking a negative pattern is that you are going directly into the resistance. However, this can be effective as well. For example, just as repeating "I'm angry" or "I'm worthless" can stir up patterns, so can positive statements. If, for example, you simply affirm "I'm worthy, I'm worthy, I'm worthy," you can stir up your worthiness issues.

Any affirmation that strongly conflicts with your deeply held beliefs can be used to activate patterns. It is a good way to get in touch with yourself in a very short time. Once your mind understands that you're not afraid to feel your feelings and make changes, you will find it easier and easier to get a clear response.

It is also useful to make longer, more involved affirmations by saying them intently and by allowing the feelings to surface after each one. Then, depending on your choice, continue either to repeat your affirming message or clear the feelings that surface from it. Remember, the affirmations are the opposite of what you still believe, and therefore, when said properly, they will cause a conflict that you can feel and work with. A long affirmation might be:

1. I am loving, kind, and giving, and create beautiful relationships.
2. I am ready and available to give and receive unconditional love.
3. I am worthy at all levels of my being, from the top of my head to the tip of my toes.

If you practice what you have learned in this chapter, you will be very pleased, maybe even a little amazed by it all.

CHAPTER 14

CANCER IMAGERY

Working with cancer patients has been a particular interest of mine. This chapter contains some images that are useful in helping to fight cancer.

Unfortunately, the use of imagery in helping patients with cancer has been badly misunderstood, and its value has been taken out of context so that to its detractors, it is held up as deceptive or even a "dangerous" form of treatment. To its stronger proponents, its case has been somewhat overstated. In my experience, I have treated, known, and worked with practitioners who have used imagery with cancer patients who were given essentially no chance to live; and yet some of them are alive and well today, even though not all were able to achieve that level of success.

By the same token, I would not say that imagery was the sole reason for their recovery. Rather, I believe that those individuals made a major personality transformation and that imagery was a factor in that transformation. In fact, I would go so far as to say that for the directed kind of cancer-destroying imagery to be effective, one clear unobstructed belief must exist within these individuals: "I am willing to do or say anything necessary to get well." If that belief is not clear at an unconscious level, certain images are not going to be effective.

The images you will do at the end of this chapter are directly connected with unconscious beliefs, which I discussed in

Chapter 10. They are useful in gauging the effectiveness of other, more "killing images." The images used in these exercises are intended to activate the immune system, which is believed to be involved in the creation of cancer. Thus, theoretically, if the immune system is weakened, activating it through mental processes could help to fight the cancer. The immune system is quite literally your body's defense system, so that any imagined metaphor for it should be able to activate the system. Before moving on to those exercises, let's look at the immune system in more depth.

MIND, IMAGERY, AND THE IMMUNE SYSTEM

In 1981, I began to study relationships that might exist between the mind and the immune system. At the time there were only a handful of scientific papers on the subject. These studies indicated that certain immune system cells appeared to be affected by depression. This was the beginning of my interest in the subject that is now called *psychoneuro-immunology*—that is, how the mind, through the nervous system, affects the immune system. This infant school of thought has become a major focus of immunology research, and thousands of scientific papers have been published.

For simplicity, you can divide the immune system into two branches—the humoral and the cellular—whose purposes are to protect you from invaders. The humoral portion seems primarily concerned with immunity against viral diseases, such as polio, the common cold, and certain bacterial infections. The cellular, meanwhile, seems to deal with specific types of infections, such as those from parasites and tuberculosis. It also controls the body's reactions to foreign grafts, such as other people's kidneys or hearts.

In practice, the systems interact constantly and aren't really separate in that sense. There is, however, one type of outsider that seems to be involved with the cellular immune system: cancer. A decrease in cellular immunity seems to leave a person particularly vulnerable to some types of cancer. One theory as to why you get cancer suggests that it is because of a breakdown in the effectiveness of this cellular immunity. AIDS, which is not cancer but a viral disease, also seems to be most destructive to the cellular portion of the immune system, and much study has been done to unravel the mysteries of cellular immunity. Recalling that the focus here is the effect of the mind on the body, research has shown that stress of various types, including depression, affects the cellular immune system. It also shows that there are definite chemical and nervous system links between the brain and the immune system. The level of the brain that affects the immune system is the level where thoughts enter. It appears that many sad thoughts—or even one—can make the body less immune. However, it still has not been shown that these thoughts lead to a breakdown such as cancer or AIDS. In my opinion, such a day is not far off.

Meantime, this is at least one reason imagery may be helpful in fighting cancer. Interestingly, the data supporting greater susceptibility to infectious agents is even stronger, and so it seems that scientists are on the right track.

We can all hope for some definitive answer someday, but today you can speak to your immune system through your mind and give it the messages you want it to hear. The following, then, is not so much an imagery technique as it is a series of suggestions for improved performance from your immune system, which may prove helpful.

TALKING TO THE IMMUNE SYSTEM

Because this next exercise is long and complex, I recommend that you have someone read it to you. Find a comfortable position, either sitting or lying, and relax yourself by following some of the exercises from earlier chapters. As you listen, mentally repeat these words to yourself.

I would like to address you, my immune system, at the deepest level of my being. You are my defense system and, just like me, are too important not to love and care for. I speak to you now so that you are of one mind in all that you do. You are loved and I want you to feel loved.

Deep down inside at the deepest level of my being, you are growing stronger and stronger, more and more clear and focused without fear, doubt, or hesitation as to your true purpose. You can and will protect me and know well your true identity. You are to be sharp and clear and recognize myself from all invaders, and you have my deepest respect and gratitude for doing so.

You are right to be strong and aggressive, but always maintain the perfect balance so that the help you give is the perfect amount. You operate at full power, always do your job but no more than is absolutely required. When there

are invaders, you will continue to attack

until the job is done. You always follow through. I can rely on you. I can trust you. You will use all resources until the job is done, returning to perfect balance and harmony when it is over. You are wise and cannot be fooled by look-alikes.

You have the perfect capacity to know exactly what does and doesn't belong within me. You can also recognize what is harmless, and so my friends, dogs, cats, bees (add anything you are allergic to), and all of nature's creatures need not be fought against. Let them be one with me and I with them. I do not wish them harm, and they will not harm me. I empower you to protect me from that which does not belong, helping to make me strong and healthy again. You, my immune system, will do this from this moment forward, every minute, every hour of the day, while I am awake and while I sleep, never stopping until the job is done. As I return to my everyday life now, I trust that it will be done as I have asked. I am now returning to my everyday state of mind strong, powerful, and refreshed.

The preceding series of suggestions, or affirmations, is useful in several circumstances. As you have seen throughout this book, you are encouraged to talk to yourself, which means your unconscious mind. You talk to yourself as a way of knowing your true beliefs and desires and of discovering ways to help yourself. It is also part of the beliefs that you can communicate with your mind and directly affect your body.

It is this mind-to-body connection you hope to affect with respect to diseases, such as cancer, AIDS, and a number of immunological disorders like rheumatoid arthritis and lupus, which also do their damage when the immune system becomes overzealous and starts attacking your own body. Common allergens, such as dogs, cats, pollen, and foods like tomatoes and eggs, are often the result of an overexcitable immune system. The monologue to yourself addresses this in a minor way also. As always, it is to be understood that any individual image or technique is to be thought of as only one part of the program.

Years ago when I did a lot of hypnosis, I was successfully able to "persuade" some people out of their allergies to many things, cats being the most prevalent. So you can see that it is possible to change many of these quasi-diseases, and, with the help of nutrition, to an even greater degree. I recommend making an audiotape of the foregoing monologue and playing it over and over to get the optimum effect.

Now let's return to the cancer imagery exercises mentioned earlier.

Soldiers on Parade

Sitting comfortably in the neutral position, take some deep breaths and try to put yourself into a relaxed state of mind. Read the following paragraphs or have someone read them to you.

Imagine you are a general standing at a reviewing stand reviewing your troops. See them coming from your left side marching past you two by two at a brisk pace. When a few have marched by, command them to slow down by saying or thinking it. After they have slowed, have them go faster again.

Now have them stop, do an about face, and begin again to move as you command. If these are your troops and they respect your command, they should do your bidding. The basic concept is to create a soldier—or anything you choose—to represent a group of individuals who are under your command. Command them and see if they obey. If they do not obey, or if they are sloppy or reluctant, you must do the following exercises to work with them.

Dialogue with the Troops

If you experience any resistance to your commands, try to find out why. Simply talk to the image—the soldiers or whatever you have imagined—and generally it will respond. Talk to the troops by thinking what you wish to say in your mind. Say, for example, "Why aren't you obeying me?" The soldiers, in my experience, are usually quite willing to give you valuable information about why they are not following your commands. The response you receive determines how you proceed.

You want to know what part of your unconscious mind objects to you as the conscious general. Is the unconscious mind, through the movement of the soldiers, saying in effect that you are not in command of your life? Does that mean someone or something else *is* in command? Who? Find out what you can do to get them to obey you. What can you do to gain more control over your life?

Depending on what comes out of that discussion, you have several options. One is to make some minor adjustment in your thinking and/or technique and have the soldiers obey and feel satisfied that you have taken command, and move on to the next exercise. If you do not get any constructive dialogue going, you may wish to keep pressuring your troops to act, which may help to force the issue. You may, however, have to go back and study earlier chapters. When you have learned more about yourself, come back, and I'm sure you'll find the exercise much more fruitful. You will not be able to get your immune system to act on your behalf unless these other problems, such as who is directing your life, get resolved.

You need to ask yourself, "Do I really want to keep living as I am living now, or are there some big changes required?" In my experience, those who did exceptionally well with immune system imagery did so not because they had great imaginations but because they changed the entire focus of their lives. Often, from their family's viewpoint, they became very different people.

When you are ready to proceed, I recommend the following exercise.

Command and Attack

Continuing in your relaxed position, begin to expand your troops so that they are at your command by going four abreast, then eight, twelve, and dozens. Starting them four at a time, march them past you, commanding them to go fast, slow, right, left, or kneel, so that you are certain that there is no resistance. If you succeed for a while and then find they get out of line, prepare to dialogue again, moving back and forth between imagery and dialogue. You must understand what you are doing and why.

Next, assemble as many troops as you can see in an area the size of a football field. Now is also the time to transform them into something else, if soldiers were not what you had envisaged to fight cancer. The football field can become an ocean filled with sharks, wild dogs, knights in shining armor, or whatever represents in your mind the most reliable, aggressive, tenacious defenders in your battle.

When this is clear, if you have not already done so, decide how to represent the cancer. Say to your mind, "Give me my *deep down inside* image of cancer." What appears will also tell you something about how you must wage your battle. You *do not* need a medically accurate picture of a cancer cell; your mind perfectly understands any symbol you choose. When you have chosen, you are ready for the final step.

With your defenders at the ready, march, swim, ride, or move them in whatever manner to where the cancer is. Command them to attack the cancer by simply intending that they do so. The cancer can be visualized as anything at all, so you may decide that you wish to change your team in mid-battle. It makes no difference as long as you are focused and organized as you do so. See, know, and expect the cancer to die as you do this. Think of the cancer as weak and stupid and yourself as strong, courageous, and powerful. Continue the action for several minutes. Periodically, breathe in white light to clear the area. And then go on.

If there is chemotherapy or radiation in your system, know that the cancer cells are even weaker. You may be able to see the drugs or radiation as an additional powerful force or ally, such as a golden light. Note the activity on the battlefield. If you do not see the cancer dying, you may need to dialogue once again, pull your team back, and regroup momentarily.

Cancer patients, in my experience, are notoriously poor at confrontation. This is a major confrontation. As you go through this process, you are constantly attending to how you think and feel to discover ways to improve the situation.

It's better to imagine this scene many times throughout the day for short periods, five minutes or less, than to go for extended periods. For those of you who aren't comfortable killing anything—even cancer—understand that healthy cells are constantly dying and being remade within your body every moment of every day. You are always killing bacteria, viruses, yeasts, and other "pests" if you take any kind of antibiotics or receive a flu shot. Life is a constant cycle of death and rebirth. I believe this exercise can be helpful to certain individuals under the right circumstances. But, again, you must be clear to use it effectively and do it along with many of the other awareness and health-enhancement techniques described in this book.

GETTING THE MOST FROM YOUR CANCER IMAGERY

Suppose that you promised to do your visualizations to fight cancer, and everyday you made excuses why you could not do them. At some point you would have to say to yourself, "I keep making excuses. Why do I resist my practice of imagery?"

You should begin to see yourself doing the visualizations that you resist, and then sense your feelings as they appear—the uncomfortableness, the irritability. As you continue in that image, from underneath you will hear this part of yourself say something like, "I feel foolish," or "This is stupid," or "It will never work," or "It's too late." Your resistance will surface as you continue into the resistance.

You may also hear something like "I hate my cancer," "I resent having to work on myself," "It stinks," "It's unfair," "I feel cheated," or "It's a lousy deal." All of this is anger, and you must repeat "It's unfair" or "I'm angry" as your activating phrase and allow that to come up. Whatever is going to come out, allow that to be released. All the anger and other feelings that you have about doing visualization need to surface.

By discharging your feelings and understanding why you don't do what you need to do, you may then begin to do the right thing. You are allowing the visualization to reveal your resistance and to get you to do what you need to do. All of these are ways to bring to the surface feelings that are deep down inside, which you may not have been able to get to. If you work with these techniques, you will be ready to complete the real change within yourself, which is actually releasing a pattern.

CHAPTER 15

HEALING AND THE MAGIC SPIRAL

In Chapter 3, "Beliefs and Blocks," complete thoughts were represented as squiggly or wavy lines. We said a complete thought consisted of a mental portion and an emotional portion wound together. (See Figures 4 and 5 on page 22.) A blocked thought was represented as a single squiggle for simplicity (see Figure 7 on page 27). Later on in the releasing exercises we found that we could use straight lines and that a simple X would suffice to do most any type of release (the X being nothing more than a symbol for the pattern). The squiggles, or more properly the waveform or spiral representation of a pattern, have some special qualities that can be used as well to achieve healing release. Let us now begin to work with waveforms or spirals which more accurately reflect our reality.

To understand why, let us look more closely at what the waveform is really representing. If it were perfectly smooth and harmonious, we could say it was free of anger, fear, doubt, etc., and might represent peace, love, or joy. What is really the difference energetically between anger and love? According to our model there is too much of the wrong kind of energy, which we have chosen to call "negative energy," and by definition distorts the perfect wave. Part of why we think of anger as "bad" or unhealthy for us is that it draws to itself other negative anger energies, and we don't want that.

The wave though doesn't know good from bad; it's just a wave. The only thing a wave can do is be too strong or too weak, too fast *or* too slow or it can be going in the wrong direction. (See Figure 14.) The wrong direction then is only one of two possibilities. It can either be clockwise and needs to be counterclockwise or it can be counterclockwise and needs to be clockwise.

POLARITY AND THE SPIRAL WAVE

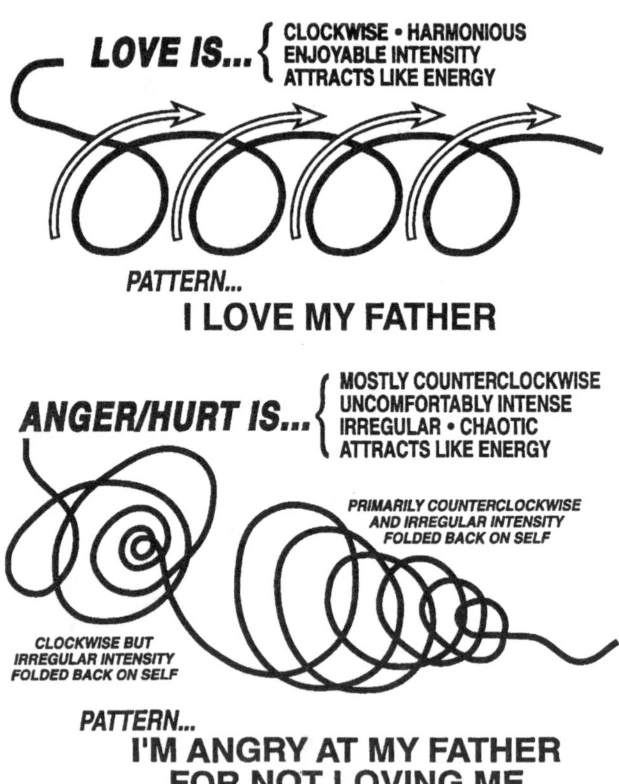

Figure 14

Negativity is our way of saying something is going in the wrong direction. For example, in the pattern "I'm angry at my father for not giving me enough love," several possibilities now exist. The anger is the "wrong direction" for you because it might keep you from loving someone or letting yourself be loved for fear of being hurt, the result of your anger. Your behavior towards a loving person then might be the *opposite* of what you really need to do, which is reach out and embrace that love. Your false belief makes you do, in effect, what is the opposite of your best interest. Energetically, it is also spinning around inside of you in opposite ways as well.

Notice that in the figure the negativity is not only flowing counterclockwise, it also goes backwards folded in on itself. The heavy or dark energy often ascribed to pain or negativity is energy that is densely folded back on itself. These dark energies can actually be felt and seen with training but this is not necessary to achieve release. One way to release then would be to reverse the direction the wave is spinning (called its polarity) and make it go the opposite direction (clockwise or counterclockwise). At the same time as the energy is redirected oppositely, the irregularities in intensity tend to smooth out automatically. In that sense, calmness or relaxation is a natural by-product of reversing the polarity.

We can use this polarity principle in a number of different ways to help us. If deep down inside you are afraid to confront your spouse about an issue, and you keep it locked up inside, isn't that the opposite of what you really need to do? Don't you need to go out from yourself and express yourself—the polar opposite of the direction you are now going? Isn't that the correct direction you should be going? In many ways, we are always doing the opposite of what we need to and reversing the polarities of the energy is one way to conceptualize this.

As before, if we know what we want to do and how we want to believe, we can bypass a lot of the unnecessary intellectualizing that often gets in the way and let our bodies do the work for us.

SPIRAL RELEASE TECHNIQUES

1. The Spiral as a Pattern

Once again we are going to symbolize the pattern we wish to release but now we will use a spiral instead. Which spiral you may ask? How do I choose? Now the fun begins. You may use the one below, in Figure 15, as a generic spiral. Your spiral must be sufficiently complex to hold some energy; otherwise, it won't work very well. It can be simple but needs to have at least four or five good twists and turns to be most effective. You may also pick up a pencil, think of the pattern, let your mind guide your hand, and you will have a picture. You may also simply command your mind and say, "Show me the spiral that best fits the pattern." Your mind will comply and you need only draw what you see. Remember, the mind likes these little games; it wants you to be creative. Part of the function of your mind is to create; so create.

ADEQUATE GENERIC SPIRAL
(COMPLEX PATTERNS HOLD MORE ENERGY)

INADEQUATE GENERIC SPIRAL
(TOO SIMPLE TO HOLD ENERGY)

Figure 15

To begin, let's first choose a pattern. For example, "I feel unworthy to receive love unless I am special." Now pick a spiral that matches the pattern. (Remember you have to pick the pattern first when creating your own because your mind has its own wisdom about which spiral will work best.) Sitting in the neutral position, see the spiral in front of you. Begin activating the pattern as before and use your mind to undo the spiral so that it basically becomes flat or just a little bumpy with small harmonious little waves. (See Figure 16.)

GENERIC SPIRAL

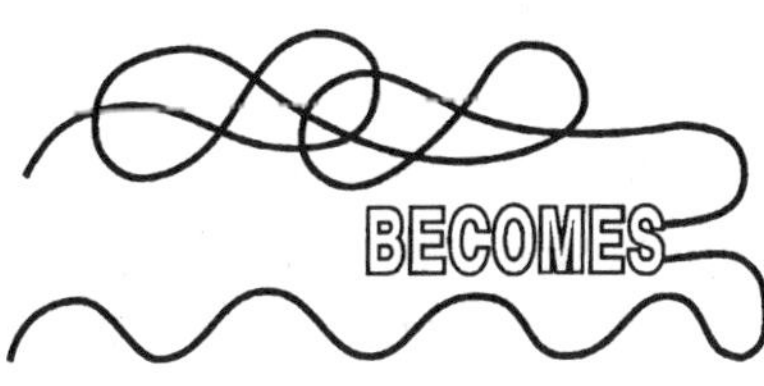

Figure 16

As you undo the spiral, breathe into it using the breath to help smooth it out. A good hard push with the breath will be very effective in smoothing your unruly spiral. And it will be unruly. It will resist and your body will resist as well. You are, however, free to move your body in whatever direction is necessary to do the smoothing. You may find yourself twisting and turning in your chair. You may even find that standing will allow you more freedom, so get up and twist and turn your body in whatever way is necessary to clear the pattern. (For you music buffs, I have a visual for you. If you have ever seen Stevie Wonder singing and moving to the music, he is following the waves of the music.)

Actually, certain kinds of music with a slow enough rhythm will get most people swaying back and forth. If you can move your body like that, it will be much easier to release the pattern. By smoothing the pattern you are still releasing energy. It is important to ground it, so continue to direct the energy downward from the chest. From mid-chest and above, you may find that coughing and gagging or crying with the mouth wide open gives the best release.

I think you can see why this exercise comes at the end after you've done some releasing. This exercise requires a bit more body awareness and comfort with the movement of energy through you. If you're still not quite comfortable with your body moving by itself as the energy comes through, you will need to work up to this one.

2. The Double Spiral Release

This is by far the most sophisticated technique for release as it combines the spiral concepts with the effect of the X as a "block."

Look at Figure 17. We now have a block similar to the X, but it is two spirals together that unravel to create two harmonious waves. What makes this technique more powerful is that each twist and turn of the individual spiral more closely represents

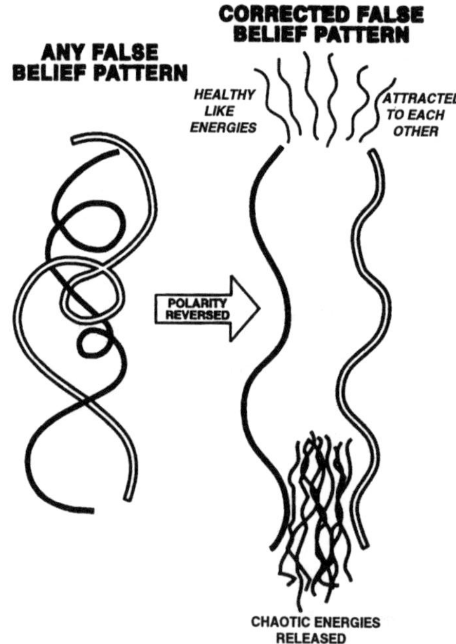

Figure 17

areas of blockage in the body. The other spiral is part of the same pattern. Since like energies attract each other, spirals attract similar, but not necessarily identical, energy forms. This represents a more accurate picture of the energies within. Where they cross can be more precisely felt as a muscle contraction, and the unraveling of the crossed areas will be felt as a relaxation of that muscle with a sense of energy flowing through. So there are two processes going on simultaneously. Each spiral needs to be undone as well as the point where they cross over so that they can be aligned parallel to each other as shown in the figure.

The process of releasing is, however, exactly the same. You must activate the pattern, breathe, and mentally undo it, which is clearly harder than a simple X, but it is much closer to the reality of the energy form of the word pattern. In that way, it is much more powerful, which means greater change for your efforts. It is the way that I personally release.

I know for some, who would like things wrapped up neat and tidy, this may seem a bit contradictory. Is it really one spiral or two? Which is best? Shall I use the X or not? A lot will depend on your level of skill and comfort with your body. The better answer is that in the realm of the mind there are no absolutes and only various levels of metaphor may be used to achieve similar results.

It is also a question that relates to the very nature of healing. A headache can be relieved by breathing techniques, meditation, massage, acupuncture, Advil™, or a powerful orgasm. What is the treatment of choice? Which is better? Faster? Safer? Cheaper? Healthier? That is part of your learning—to discern what is best for you. Having said all of the above, and perhaps making it sound a little more difficult than it really is, I now present you with something as easy and gentle as a summer's breeze.

3. Spiral Quick Release

This is a very quick, one-minute version of the spiral technique, especially good for tension or pain. Tension and pain are really compacted energies. Here the polarity concept can be applied by thinking of pain or tension as something that is screwed in. Most things in our world, like screws and light bulbs, are screwed in or tightened by turning clockwise. Imagine a screwdriver in your hand. When you put something in the wall you're basically twisting your wrist to the right to put it in and twisting left or counterclockwise to take it out.

UNSCREWING THE PAIN Imagine your pain or tension as a dense black screw screwed into your body (see Figure 18). Now simply imagine it being screwed out of your body into space. As you are doing it, be as relaxed as possible and think to yourself, "I am releasing this deepest pain," and the pain will begin to dissipate. If you know some patterns associated with the pain, repeat them, activating them as you have been taught, and unscrew the pattern as well. You might find great success in releasing this way, which is easier than the first two methods. Regardless of which method you choose, let your body move freely and let the energies move your body without trying to control it.

Figure 18

CHAPTER 16

SHARING THE ENERGY EXPERIENCE

Part of what makes life fun is sharing our experiences. Even going to the movies doesn't seem quite the same by ourselves (even if no words are spoken throughout the entire movie). What could be better than sharing our energies? Of course, in real life we are always sharing whether or not we are aware of it. The rare times we can share a birth or a death together can be one of the most profound, ineffable experiences human beings can have. We share miseries and joys of all kinds, and routinely sex is seen as one of the most intense. But every compliment and every sarcastic remark is, in effect, an energy exchange as well. We are constantly picking up the feelings of others around us whether we want to or not. We all know that we are, but we are rarely cognizant of how much they affect us and how powerful our feelings, both positive and negative, help or harm the ones we love.

In this next series of exercises you will begin to sense just how much we affect each other at the unspoken level. After discovering your power, we will then proceed to techniques that you can use to help the ones you love to release and heal.

THE ENERGY BALL

Preparatory to working with your partner, you need to literally grab hold of the energies that flow to and through you so you can sense their reality. You and your partner, working separately, must begin by getting a little more relaxed—energy flows best when the body is relaxed.

Sit comfortably with your feet flat on the floor and take three good, deep breaths. Rub your hands together until you feel some heat. Slowly pull your hands apart a few inches, then a little more. At about six inches begin to move your hands back together, but do not let them touch (it will be a little bit like playing an accordion). As you move them back and forth, sense the attraction—a pulsing—that exists between your hands. (See Figure 19.)

THE ENERGY BALL

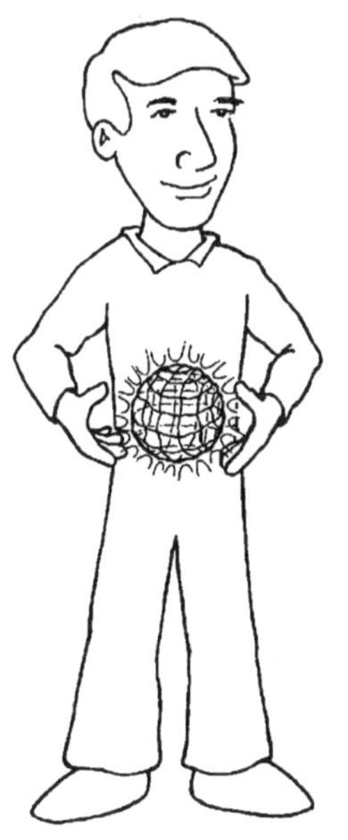

Figure 19

Let them touch and once again begin rubbing them together. This time imagine that an orange ball of light exists between your hands and as you move your hands back and forth, think to yourself, "My energy is growing stronger and stronger." Notice how that affects the attraction you feel between your palms. Do this exercise until you can feel the energy that exists between your hands and are convinced that it is real. When that feels right, you are ready to work with your partner.

EXCHANGING ENERGIES

One person is designated as the sender and the other as the receiver. The receiver is passive and just thinks to him/herself, "I will receive whatever energies are sent to me." The sender will then transmit different feelings and the receiver will sense them after which you will switch sides and return the favor. (See Figure 20.)

EXCHANGING ENERGIES

Figure 20

Begin this way: You (the sender) should start by rubbing your hands together, as before, to get the energies going. When you are satisfied that you can feel the energies (tingles in your hand), your (the sender) right hand comes up to the receiver's left hand without touching, palm to palm about a half an inch apart. You think to yourself, "Flow, I am sending the perfect flow," and repeat that periodically for about a minute or so. Slow, deep breaths with slow prolonged exhalations will increase the feelings. When the receiver acknowledges that he feels something, he should say so but nothing more. It is not necessary to say anything more. Rest if you are tired, otherwise continue on this way.

Next the sender thinks, "I care so much. I love (my spouse, parent, other) so much." Transmit that feeling through your palm. The sender will send for about a minute. When the receiver says he feels something, he should say so, but nothing more. Rest if you must, otherwise continue on. If you decide to put your hands down, to get things going again, simply rub your palms together a bit as before and begin again.

Now the sender changes his thoughts and thinks, "I'm very, very angry." Think of something real or imagined to be angry about and continue to send the feeling of anger through your palm. The sending should continue until the receiver feels something.

When you are satisfied that feelings were exchanged and acknowledged, once again it is not necessary to discuss it. Either rest or go on to repeat the neutralizing statement, "Flow, I'm sending the perfect flow." Think and send that for 30 seconds. When the previous feeling is neutralized, you are ready to send yet another feeling—fear. The sender thinks to himself, "I'm afraid of him/her. He'll/She'll hurt me. I'm afraid," and continues with fear thoughts for about a minute or so until the receiver acknowledges this new feeling. Then once again stop and neutralize it with "Flow, I'm sending the perfect flow." As a final portion of this exercise the sender once again sends love, but this time the receiver rejects it and thinks to himself, "I reject his energy, I reject his love," periodically until the sender senses something. Now discuss what came up, what each of you noticed, and when you are ready, switch places so you can both share the experience.

From this exercise you should have learned several things. First, that energy as feelings is being sent out of you by mere thought alone. Second, that different feelings feel different; anger has a different feel than fear and much different than love. Third, that it takes no great skill to send it. Fourth, and really most important of all, a person can repel another person's energy, especially love.

Receiving love is an active process in which you take in what is rightfully yours. It can be blocked or repelled unconsciously by your loved one leading to his/her sense of being unloved when, in fact, love is truly being sent. Here is perhaps one of the most classic examples of misunderstanding between caring people. If a person does not feel worthy to receive love, they are, in effect, repelling it. You can send it all day or all through a lifetime and he/she will say, "Nobody loves me." All the logic and reason, all the nice things you do for him/her, seem to have little effect. Feeling loved is an experience—an energy experience. If you do not feel it in your life, it doesn't necessarily mean it is not being sent. I know it as a therapist and I know it as a person. My siblings and father kept sending love to my mother all the time and she never got it. And because she never got it, she created for herself and her family a lot of unnecessary unhappiness.

PARTNER RELEASE TECHNIQUES

If you have done the exercises above successfully, you know that feelings are real, and they can be sent and received at will. There are three major ways to help a loved one release. In order to do this, it is best if the helper protects himself with a barrier of positive energy lest the helper feel the other person's negativity and some unpleasantness in anyway afterward.

If you are the helper, sit quietly for a moment and visualize a swirling cloud of white energy surrounding you and extending at least four to six inches. I personally prefer to have the energy moving very quickly around me in a counterclockwise fashion. Another way is to simply allow a powerful white light to envelope you as thick as you can make it. The specifics seem less important than the intention, and for what you will be doing, it will be quite sufficient.

1. Soaking Up the Energy

Begin with the person being helped doing the releasing, sitting in a chair or preferably lying on a couch or bed. (See Figure 21 on page 219.) A pattern is chosen to be released and he begins to use any of the standard techniques you have learned. It is important that he express initially where he feels the pattern. For example, if the pattern is "I need to feel special to receive love," the releaser would say, "I'm starting to feel it in my chest." As he continues to release in the usual manner, the helper would put her hands above, on, or around his chest with the clear intention that she is soaking up the negative energy with her left hand and putting in positive, loving energy with the right. She thinks to herself or says quietly under her breath, "I am driving out this false belief about his inability to receive love. Release, release, release this unnecessary and harmful belief." Depending on the relationship, one might then add, "Receive, receive, receive this love or healing energy that you rightfully deserve." The releaser might then say, "The energy is moving into my belly now," and the helper would do the same thing on or around the belly repeating the same phrases over and over. This would continue until the pair decides the release is over.

Any pain or discomfort could likewise be released. One could say, "My headache, my headache, my terrible headache. I am acknowledging the pain of my terrible headache and I am willing to release it now." The helper's hands would go over the releaser's head in the same fashion as before until the two were satisfied with the progress they had made. It is, of course, preferable to have a specific pattern about the headache. Regardless, you can help a great deal with just the acknowledgment of the pain itself.

When this and all the helping exercises are over, the helper should shake out the negative energy by shaking out his/her hands a few times. They should be washed in cool or cold water for a couple of minutes as well. The energies are real. Don't forget that. You don't want them sticking to you.

2.The Sweep

The concept here is basically the same. (Again, see Figure 21.) The releaser begins his pattern to be released in the same way, but the helper makes different movements with her hands. Depending on where the pattern is first felt, one or both hands are used in a sweeping motion from the mid-chest down towards the feet. The same words are repeated as above, but the helper makes continuous sweeps across his body with the intention of moving the energy towards his feet. As in the exercise above, an energy may begin in the chest and move into the belly. The figure shows one hand on the chest and another on the belly. Precise placement of the hands is not critical. It is more important to move the hands over the areas where most of the emotion is felt and then use a general sweeping motion towards the feet. In the soaking up motion, the energy may not get to his feet, but here the releaser may

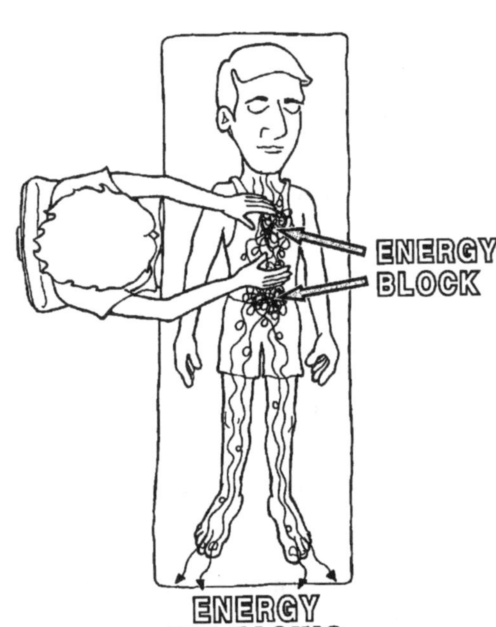

Figure 21

well feel heat or tingling in the feet as the pattern is discharged. If the energy seems higher up, begin mid-chest, or at the neck or head. The direction may be towards the mouth, with gentle tickling motions at the throat to encourage gagging, coughing or crying.

3. The Support Technique

This technique is vitally important as the vast majority of traditional therapists will not help you in this more intimate way. In time, it will be routinely accepted, but for now it's up to you.

In this technique the release begins the same way as before. A pattern is chosen and the process is begun. Generally when the pattern is very deep and painful it is very difficult for the individual to allow him/herself to experience it because he/she feels overwhelmed. The words I hear from patients are "I feel like I'll explode or fly apart or it will just blow out my circuits. I'll lose myself somehow and won't get back." This seems especially true for deep trauma like physical or sexual abuse, but others without such trauma still express this feeling of being overwhelmed by their emotions.

As the helper, you are not going to be helping to remove the energies so much as acting as support for the releaser in a very specific way. As I have discovered, the sense of literally coming apart with this tremendous sense of dread for something unspeakable keeps even the most motivated individuals from getting into their pain. However, if they feel secure and held together, then they will be able to release what they fear most.

As the releaser begins a pattern like "I am releasing my anger and hatred for my father for molesting (beating, abusing) me" and as the energy starts to surface, begin to hold him wherever it seems comfortable and appropriate. Holding a hand may be enough, but more likely holding his shoulders, or actually embracing him (but giving him enough space to do his release), will help immensely. If that is too confining or does not give enough support, a strong, firm hand down on his chest pressing quite hard, or on the belly, will keep him from feeling that he is flying apart.

Think about it yourself. If you felt that you were about to explode from the chest and you couldn't control it, how would you want to be protected? Try one way, then another.

Your releaser will tell you what works and what doesn't. As he releases, talk to him, encourage him saying, "I've got you, I won't let go, stay with it," and the like. He may need to squeeze you, so say, "Squeeze me as hard as you want. You can't hurt me. We'll come through this together." Before you were more a quiet, almost silent, partner, but now you're more like a coach getting your loved one through the last mile of the marathon.

When couples or friends do this work together the results are amazing and the feelings of closeness and love increase tremendously.

What you are doing is nothing more than an extension of your natural desire to physically support anyone you care about who is going through a difficult time. The only difference is that this difficult time may have occurred 30 years ago.

We all need to touch to feel happy and healthy. It, of course, must be wanted touch versus unwanted, which is often the source of the problem in the first place. Now you're giving it with a new clarity and specific intention, but that's the only real difference. If you are interested in doing more with healing, some reference books are listed for further study. Like the commercial says, now just get in there and do it!

Parting Thoughts

In this little guidebook, I have tried to present alternative methods to both finding and defining so-called problems as well as some unique ways to solve them. I know that these ideas will seem very radical to some and maybe counter-intuitive, but your intuition is only valuable to the extent that it is operating on the correct assumptions and is able to accurately interpret the data presented to it.

Accepting the concept of people as energy beings and problems as distorted energies is, I believe, an idea whose time has come. The 1990s are seeing much of medicine redefined as energetic relationships, and readers of this book have an advance look as this trend comes to pass. This is the decade when the mind and body will finally be rejoined as complementary systems and no longer be thought of as distinct, with one part unable to affect the other.

As I have said before, this is only the beginning of what is possible. There will be more information available, adding more pieces to the body/mind puzzle that will be both healing and transformational. I hope you will join me in that adventure, and I look forward to the opportunity to be part of this movement in the years ahead.

For now, thank you for your kind attention, and I wish you all health, peace, and prosperity.

SUGGESTED READING

There are no specific references to articles or books and I have purposely minimized the amount of scientific data which seemed unnecessary to prove the value and power of pyschoenergetics. However, there are many related and interesting titles, which touch and expand upon many of the methods described in this book that I would like to recommend.

Achterberg, Jeanne. *Imagery and Healing, Shamanism and Modern Medicine*. Boston and London: New Science Library, 1973.

Borysenko, Ph.D., Joan. *Minding the Body Mending the Mind*. New York: Bantam Books, 1987.

Bradshaw, John. *Homecoming, Reclaiming and Championing Your Inner Child*. New York: Bantam Books, 1990.

Brennan, Barbara Ann. *Hands of Light, A Guide to Healing Through the Human Energy Field*. Toronto, New York: Bantam Books, 1988.

Chopra, M.D., Deepak. *Quantum Healing*. New York: Harmony Books, 1991.

Diamond, M.D., John. *Life Energy*. New York: Dodd Mead & Co., 1985.

Feldenkrais, M. *Body and Mature Behavior, A Study of Anxiety, Sex, Gravitation and Learning*. New York, New York: International University Press, 1973.

Gerber, M.D., Richard. *Vibrational Medicine.* Sante Fe, New Mexico: Bear & Company, 1988.

Golos, Natalie. *Management of Complex Allergies, The Patients Guide.* Norwalk, Connecticut: New England Foundation of Allergic and Environmental Diseases, 1985.

Laskow, M.D., Leonard. *Healing With Love.* San Francisco, California: Harper and Rowe, 1987.

Lowen, M.D., Alexander. *The Language of the Body.* London, England: Collier Macmillan, 1971.

Lowen, Alexander and Leslie L. *A Way to Vibrant Health, A Manual of Bioenergetic Exercises.* New York: Harper and Rowe, 1977.

Montagu, Ashley. *Touching the Human Significance of the Skin.* New York: Harper and Rowe, 1987.

Pierrakos, M.D., John C. *Core Energetics.* Mendocino, California: Life Rhythum Publication, 1987.

Rama, Swami and Ballentine, Rudolph, M.D. and Hymes, M.D., Alan. *Science of Breath—A Practical Guide.* Honesdale, Pennsylvania: Himalayan International Institute of Yoga Science and Philosophy, 1979.

Index

A

B

C

G

H

I

L

M

N

T

U

V

ORDER FORM

If you know someone who would benefit from the psychoenergetic method, you can order more copies of this book by filling out the following information.

Please send______copies of *PSYCHOENERGETICS*™ to:

(Please Print)

Company name:______________________________

Name:______________________________

Address:______________________________

City:____________________State:____Zip:__________

Cost: Single copy $15.95 _______

California sales tax: _______

Postage & Handling: $ 1.75 _______

Total enclosed: _______

Please send check or money order to:

Oceanview Publishing
P.O. Box 8708, Dept. 613
Newport Beach, CA 92658-1708
Phone: 714-852-1793
Fax: 714-852-1588

If you would like to purchase tapes that reinforce the teachings in this book, use this order form and receive a 15% discount. For more information and a free demonstration tape, call or write Oceanview Publishing. To have Dr. Weiss speak to your organization please call, write or fax to the above address and phone numbers.